THE MASTER OF THE WINDS

and Other Tales from Siberia

TRANSLATED FROM THE RUSSIAN BY MIRRA GINSBURG

The Fox and the Hare

The Diary of Nina Kosterina

Azef BY ROMAN GOUL

The Master and Margarita BY MIKHAIL BULGAKOV

Heart of the Dog BY MIKHAIL BULGAKOV

Flight, A PLAY BY MIKHAIL BULGAKOV

The Life of Monsieur de Molière BY MIKHAIL BULGAKOV

Bliss, A PLAY BY MIKHAIL BULGAKOV

TRANSLATED FROM THE RUSSIAN AND EDITED

BY MIRRA GINSBURG

The Fatal Eggs and Other Soviet Satire

The Dragon BY YEVGENY ZAMYATIN

Last Door to Aiya (SOVIET SCIENCE FICTION)

A Soviet Heretic: Essays BY YEVGENY ZAMYATIN

The Ultimate Threshold (SOVIET SCIENCE FICTION)

THE MASTER OF THE WINDS
and Other Tales from Siberia

TRANSLATED AND EDITED

BY MIRRA GINSBURG

ILLUSTRATED BY ENRICO ARNO

CROWN PUBLISHERS, INC.

NEW YORK

The editor dedicates this collection
to
ISAAC BASHEVIS SINGER
a Master of the Tale
and
to the memory
of another Master and beloved friend
KORNEY CHUKOVSKY

TABLE OF CONTENTS

THE MASTER OF THE WINDS

and Other Tales from Siberia

INTRODUCTION

RUSSIA, which extends over a large area of Europe and an even larger area of Asia, is a land of infinite variety. It has forbidding mountains and rich, fertile plains; dry, hot deserts and desolate regions of perennial ice and snow; cities with populations of many millions and illimitable stretches of land where men live in tiny isolated groups dispersed over many hundreds of miles. It is a country enormously rich in natural resources and also enormously rich in the diversity of peoples who inhabit it. For in addition to the Russians—its largest national group—Russia is the home of more than one hundred different nationalities, with their own languages, traditions, and cultures. And this is why one of Russia's greatest resources is its astonishing wealth of folklore, as fascinating and as varied as the peoples who created it.

With this book, we shall begin a journey through

this little-known realm—a folktale journey from end to end of this vast land.

The first stage of this journey will be the cold Asian north—Siberia. Russians began the conquest and colonization of Siberia almost four centuries ago. They settled, however, mostly in the relatively milder, southern regions. And it is not their stories that will be told in *The Master of the Winds*, but those of the small native nationalities that inhabit the harsh areas in the north and far east.

These nationalities are small indeed. Some, like the Yukagirs, consist of only several hundred persons. Others, like the Kets, Dolgans, Russian Eskimos, and Nivkhs, number fewer than five thousand. The rest number from five to twenty thousand each. The only exception are the Yakuts, one of the largest native groups in Siberia, consisting of approximately a quarter million persons.

The lives of all these peoples are very different from ours. From time immemorial they have lived along the banks of the great Siberian rivers and the coasts of the icy northern seas, in the dense coniferous forest, the taiga, and the vast, treeless, often marshy plains known as the tundra. Here men have not imposed their will on nature, but must still obey her own harsh laws if they are to survive. For although some things have changed during our century as a result of industrial development and changes in social organization, much remains as it has been for ages past.

Some of these peoples, like the Mansi, Khants, Selkups, and Kets, whose chief occupations are hunting and fishing, are settled within relatively small areas. Others, like the Nentsy, Chukchi, Evenks, and Yakuts, who are engaged chiefly in reindeer breeding (the last two also breed horses and other cattle farther south), are spread over immense territories. They have led and to some extent still lead a nomadic existence, driving their herds from grazing land to grazing land in search of the lichen and mosses on which the reindeer subsist and which throughout the greater part of the year the animals must dig out from beneath the snow.

For many centuries, the sedentary peoples lived in tiny villages, often consisting of only two or three households. Their dwellings varied from semi-dugouts and log cabins to tents covered with skins in winter and birchbark or cloth in summer. The nomads lived in tents of various shapes and sizes. Travel was on foot, by skis or snowshoes, or in sleds drawn by reindeer or, in some cases, dogs. Water transportation was by canoes and small boats made of birchbark, hollowed logs, or animal skins drawn over wooden frames. Food consisted principally of meat or fish, berries, wild onions, and roots dug up in the forest or the tundra. In rare cases, some cereals were obtained from Russians or even grown in milder areas under Russian influence.

Although these northern peoples led lives of extreme isolation, they were not completely cut off from the rest of the world. They traded with one another. Reindeer herders bartered their products for those of the hunters and fishermen. Once a year they journeyed to remote government centers to pay their tax, usually in sable skins. They also made long journeys to trading posts or fairs to sell their furs to Russian merchants (or, in the East, also to Chinese merchants) and buy from them such things as cloth, tea, and antiquated guns, although much of the hunting was done with bow and arrows, traps, and snares.

Yet, incredibly hard as their life seems to us, there was richness and gaiety in it as well. Their clothes, usually made of animal skins, were skillfully decorated with appliqués of fur, bright cloth, and silk, and embroidered with wool and beads. Their implements were carved with intricate designs. They held festivals, often before hunting and fishing expeditions, often after their successful completion. At these festivals there were religious ceremonies, usually conducted by the shamans—priests, sorcerers, and medicine men. There were also games and contests of strength and skill, such as races, wrestling matches, and archery.

And, of course, they fashioned and told an endless variety of legends, fables, and tales—about animals, about the daily life of the people and the adventures of legendary heroes, about supernatural beings and magical transformations, about evil forces and the fight against them, ending sometimes in victory, at other times in defeat.

There were stories of love and loss and search, of death and resurrection, like "The Crane's Feather," tender little tales like "The Lost Song," mocking tales and fables like "The Enemy Tent" and "The Wise Owl," tales of weird beings like "The Ninwits," and playful, humorous tales like "A Long Night's Sleep" and "The Maiden and the Moon."

These tales, like all great literature, encompass many elements. "The Singing Man," for example, is at the same time a lovely story of magical adventure, a vivid, graphic picture of life in the north, and a biography of a poet (all poets, all artists, perhaps all men who seek to find and realize their own selves). Kunachi, half human, half divine, is helpless in man's daily world. It is only when he is called, when he must find himself and gather his resources, when he goes forth alone to face his own trials and achieve his own destiny, when he refuses the worldly temptations of wealth and power, that he is given the gift—the simplest, smallest, but most precious gift of vision and of song. Yet this astonishingly profound tale is told so simply, in such concrete detail, that we also learn how the people who created it lived, how they obtained their food and clothing, how they and their neighbors survived in their harsh, demanding land. We learn how the northern peoples hunted, fished, traded with the Russians who came in ships, how they adorned their clothes and implements, how they played and sang and danced, and how they regarded the world around them.

This is true of the other tales as well. Beyond their wisdom, humor, beauty, and imaginative power, they are, each in its own way, both a reflection of the lives of their makers and an expression of their ideas and beliefs. Taken together, they provide a remarkably detailed and accurate picture of life in the Siberian north.

When the devil in "Khasynget's Grandmother" says, "There is no one around, no one less than a day's journey away, save you and me," we immediately know and feel the enormous isolation of the region. "The Master of the Winds" tells us about the precariousness of man's life in the stormy north. We see the dwellings of the Nenets people in the snowy, wind-swept plain, we see how clothing is made by the women from animal hides brought home by the hunters. We discover the virtues needed for survival and admired by the people: loyalty, courage, endurance, kindness, diligence, skill, and the willingness to sacrifice for the good of the family or tribe.

These qualities are also woven into the themes of such diverse stories as "The Hunter and the Tiger," "The Good Son," and the heroic and poetic tale, "Unyany." "The Mistress of Fire," which mirrors the belief that all things are inhabited by their own master spirits, speaks once again of the precariousness of man's existence and the need to respect the elements that give and sustain life.

The Master of the Winds is the first collection in a series of regional tales from Russia. Other regions have tales very different from these in both substance and detail, in form and ideas, each group reflecting a different way of life and different traditions. Very few of these tales have appeared in English before. Many of them have been collected and recorded by Russian scholars and writers only in recent decades, and are virtually as new to their Russian readers as they will be to the children and, hopefully, adults who read them in this country.

THE WISE OWL

A Mansi Tale

he Upper Spirit Topal-Oyka sat one day with his wife at the window of their house. His wife said:

"Who are you, Topal-Oyka?"

"What do you mean, who am I? I am the Upper Spirit."

"Well, if you are the Upper Spirit, why do you live in such a poor house?"

"What is wrong with our house?" Topal-Oyka asked with astonishment. "I like it."

"Men have houses just like this. It isn't right for the Upper Spirit to live in such a house. Build yourself a new, tall, spacious house that will amaze everyone who sees it, that will be praised by everyone."

"But what can I build such a house with?" asked the Upper Spirit Topal-Oyka.

"Bones would do very well," advised his wife.

"But where can I get so many bones?"

"It is very simple," his wife replied. "Gather all the animals, birds, and fish, and kill them. Then you will have enough bones to build a new house."

"I suppose it can be done," said Topal-Oyka. "Very well, we'll do it."

He sent the pike to call the fish, the nimble ermine to call the animals, and the long-legged sandpiper to call the birds.

After a short while the fish came swimming, the animals came running, and birds came flying in answer to Topal-Oyka's call. The Upper Spirit Topal-Oyka came out, counted them, and said:

"All the animals are here, and all the fish. But the birds are not all here. The owl did not come. Did you see the owl, sandpiper?"

"No, I didn't," the sandpiper answered.

"Run out and find her," said Topal-Oyka. "If I am going to kill you, I want to kill everybody at once."

The long-legged sandpiper ran to look for the owl. He looked for a long time, and at last he found her. She was sitting on a tall cedar tree.

"Why are you sitting there, owl? Didn't you hear the call?"

"Whose call?"

"Topal-Oyka's. He is gathering all the fish and birds and beasts."

"What for?"

"He'll kill us all, and build a new house with our bones. Topal-Oyka's wife does not like the old house."

"I see!" said the owl. "In that case, run along, and I will follow later."

The sandpiper ran back.

"Did you find the owl?" asked Topal-Oyka.

"I did."

"Where is she?"

"She sits on the cedar tree. She said she'll come later."

They waited and waited, but the owl was not there.

"Run back and see what is delaying her!"

The long-legged sandpiper ran for the owl again. She still sat quietly on the cedar tree.

"Well, why aren't you coming?" cried the sandpiper. "Everybody is waiting for you."

"In that case, there is no need to hurry," said the owl. "I'll sit and think some more. After all, I must think both for myself and for you, since you don't know how to do it for yourselves. Go, I will follow."

The sandpiper came back, breathless with all that running. After he caught his breath, he said:

"The owl is coming."

Again everyone waited, and again she did not come. Topal-Oyka became angry at the sandpiper.

"Run for her again, but don't came back without her!"

The sandpiper set out for the third time. But the owl had not even shifted her feet on the branch. She was sitting just as before. The sandpiper cried to her:

"I've no more strength to run after you! And Topal-Oyka is angry!"

The owl stretched her wings, flapped them, and circled over the sandpiper.

"You see, I'm flying. And now run again for the last time as fast as you can and tell Topal-Oyka's wife to open a window in her house."

The sandpiper came running back.

"The owl is flying behind m :. She said you were to open a window in the house."

They opened a window, and just at that moment the owl appeared. She sat down on the sill, her tail inside the house, her beak looking out.

"Where were you when I called? asked Topal-Oyka.

The owl was silent.

"Why don't you answer?"

"I am thinking," said the owl.

"What about?" asked Topal-Oyka.

"I am wondering: Are there more green trees on earth, or are there more dry ones?"

"You are stupid," said Topal-Oyka. "There are more green trees on earth."

"Huh!" said the owl. "It only seems so. What I say is that if a tree is dried out at the core, it will dry out soon, anyway, even if it is still green. And so it can be counted among the dry ones."

"That is right, it's a clever thought," said Topal-Oyka. "When a tree begins to dry out, it will die. There is nothing you can do about it!"

"I am also wondering," said the owl. "If you take all the birds and the fish and the beasts, are there more live ones among them, or more dead ones?"

"Naturally, there are more live ones," said Topal-Oyka. "What a silly question."

"And I say this isn't so," said the owl. "You've gathered us all here to kill us and make a new house with our bones. We are as good as dead. And soon there will be no live ones left at all."

"That's right, too!" cried Topal-Oyka. "Why didn't I think of it before?"

And the owl was silent again. And everybody was silent. Finally, Topal-Oyka lost his patience.

"Haven't you finished thinking yet?"

"I haven't finished," replied the owl. "What do you

think: Are there more men in the world, or more women?"

"There is no need to think about that," laughed Topal-Oyka. "Of course, there are more men. Will you say it's not so?"

The owl shook her head:

"That depends on how you look at it! What would you say: If a man lives by someone else's mind and not his own, would you call him a man?"

"No! A man like that is not a man!"

"You're saying that about yourself, Topal-Oyka," said the owl. "You're not a man!"

"What do you mean, I'm not a man?" cried the Upper Spirit.

"Just that! When you were creating the beasts and the birds and the fish, you did not ask anyone's advice. Then you were a man. But now you listen to your foolish wife. To please her whim, you want to kill us all. I won't be killed. I sat down with my back to the room and my beak facing out. I'll flap my wings and fly away. And to everyone I meet, I will shout: Topal-Oyka is not a man! He lives by the mind of a stupid woman, not by his own!"

Topal-Oyka heard that and felt ashamed.

"Wait, don't fly away!" he said to the owl. "And you, birds, beasts, and fish, go back to where you came from. I will not kill you. I like my old house well enough. And my wife can do as she pleases."

Everyone rejoiced. The fish swam away, the birds flew away, the animals ran, each to his own home.

And the owl sat there, her yellow eyes burning.

"Well, what do you think now?" asked Topal-Oyka. "You will not say to everyone that I am not a man?"

"I'll think about it some more," said the owl. "No, perhaps I will not say that now."

KHASYNGET'S GRANDMOTHER

A Khant Tale

rouse was the devil's favorite dish. He had many snares set out on Grouse Hill. Every spring the grouse gathered on Grouse Hill from all the forests around to send out their mating calls. They were so many that their feet had trampled the whole hilltop bare, and grass no longer grew there. And the devil's snares were never empty.

Not far from Grouse Hill lived Khasynget with his old grandmother. Khasynget was also fond of grouse, but he was too lazy to do his own hunting. And so he stole the birds from the devil's snares. At first he would steal one, then two, and then he began to empty all the snares.

The devil would come and find nothing at all. He

would set out the snares again, but the next day they would be empty again. Well, the devil was no fool. He guessed that someone must be getting at his catch. One evening he hid in the bushes and stayed there all night. And in the morning he caught Khasynget at his stealing.

"Why do you take my grouse?" the devil shouted.

"I take my own," answered Khasynget.

"What do you mean, your own? These snares are mine!"

"The snares may be yours, but the grouse are mine. The whole Grouse Hill is mine. Ask anyone you wish."

"Whom can I ask?" wondered the devil. "There is no one around, no one less than a day's journey away, save you and me!"

"You can ask God," said Khasynget. "He knows everything."

The devil was even more astonished.

"How can I ask God?"

"I'll tell you how. Come to the old fir tree tomorrow morning, the one by the river, and there we'll ask God who owns Grouse Hill."

The devil went away. And Khasynget ran to his grandmother.

"Grandmother," he said. "Tomorrow morning I'll put you up in a birch basket in the old fir tree. Sit quietly and don't move. If I ask you a question, answer. If anybody else asks, keep quiet."

And so he did. Before the sun had risen, he lifted up his grandmother into the fir tree and sat down on the river bank. The sun rose, and the devil came.

"Well," said Khasynget to the devil. "You ask God first. Let's hear what he will say."

The devil raised his head and shouted:

"Hey, God, who is the master of Grouse Hill?"

But Grandmother did not say a word.

"God is silent," said the devil. "Now you ask him."

Khasynget raised his head and shouted:

"Hey, God, is Grouse Hill mine?"

"Yours, yours!" cried the grandmother.

She cried so loudly that she jumped. The branch gave way, and the basket with Grandmother fell into the water with a loud splash.

"What was that?" asked the devil.

"Oh, nothing! A fir cone dropped into the water," said Khasynget, and thought to himself: "I really ought to pull Grandmother out of the river, but the devil will guess that I fooled him. Oh, well, let me finish one thing, then I'll take care of the other."

"Well, then," said the devil. "I suppose it is true that Grouse Hill belongs to you. There is nothing more for me to do here, I'll move on to some other place. You can keep my snares."

The devil went away. Khasynget was so glad that he forgot all about his grandmother and began to set the snares.

And the basket with the grandmother was caught up by the current and carried downstream. The basket rocked on the waves as it floated. Soon it turned around one curve, then another.

A school of young fish swarmed over to see what was rocking in the water. They saw the grandmother and said:

"Grandma, Grandma, we are many, let us push your basket ashore."

"No, little ones, don't push me. If my own grandson is not running down the river after me, it means he does not need me. Let the river carry me where it will."

The young fish flipped their tails and swam away. And the basket sailed on.

Suddenly some salmon raised their heads out of the water. They saw the grandmother and their round eyes goggled at her.

"Grandma, Grandma, look out, your basket will get soaked and you will drown. Let us push you toward the bank."

"No, my dears, don't do it," said the grandmother. "If my own grandson is not looking for me, it means he does not love me. Let the river do with me as it will."

The salmon splashed and disappeared.

The basket sailed, the grandmother rocked on the waves. The river grew wider, then narrower. It flowed straight, then it turned and twisted. And finally the basket was caught in the root of a tree, and could move neither forward nor back, neither right nor left.

Three sturgeons swam over to the basket and asked:

"Grandma, Grandma, why are you rocking in the middle of the river? Let us push your basket ashore!"

And the grandmother answered:

"Well, push it, if you have a mind to! I guess the river does not want to carry me any farther."

The sturgeons struck the basket with their tails, and it moved off the root. They nudged it with their noses, and Grandmother sailed toward shore. Before she knew it, she was out on the sand. The sturgeons waved their tails to her and went off on their own sturgeon business.

Grandmother stepped on the ground and looked around her. The spot was nice enough, with a wood nearby, and the river to supply her with food and water.

And the grandmother settled there. She put up a birchbark tent, picked berries, caught fish.

Everything would have been fine, but she felt lonely without her grandson.

"Where is Khasynget now?" she wondered. "How is he living there without me? Better or worse?"

One day she saw someone coming along the bank. She looked again, and it was Khasynget. He came over and sat down by the fire. His grandmother asked him:

"Why aren't you living alone, my grandson? Why aren't you catching grouse on Grouse Hill?"

And Khasynget answered:

"I fooled the devil. I thought I'd outsmart him, but he was more cunning than I. He left me Grouse Hill, but he took the grouse with him. I'm in a bad way, Grandmother, I'm hungry."

"Eh, Grandson," said his grandmother, "you tried to fool someone, and he fooled you. You took up with the devil and left your own grandmother to the mercy of the waves. Well, if you are hungry, what can I do with you? How can I send you away?"

The grandmother felt sorry for her grandson and fed him.

Khasynget ate and said:

"Forgive me, Grandma! I was a bad grandson. I guess the devil snared me like a grouse."

And they began to live together again.

Khasynget went out to hunt and fish. Grandmother cooked the food and made the clothes. Each to his own tasks, and each looking after the other.

THE MASTER
OF THE WINDS

A Nenets Tale

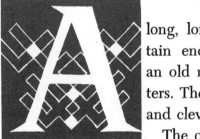long, long time ago, in a certain encampment, there lived an old man with three daughters. The youngest was the best and cleverest of the three.

The old man was very poor. His tent was shabby and full of holes. Neither he nor his daughters had enough warm clothes. When it was very cold, they all sat around the fire to keep warm. At night, they put out the fire and went to bed. But even in bed they shivered with the cold.

One day, in the middle of winter, a terrible snowstorm arose in the tundra. The wind howled, driving great gusts of blinding snow all day long, threatening to blow away the tents and leaving the people without shelter. The storm lasted and lasted—a day, two days, three days. The people could not come out of their tents, they could not go fishing or hunting. Their food was all eaten, and everyone was hungry.

The old man sat with his three daughters in the tent, listening to the wild howling of the storm. And he said to his daughters:

"This is not an ordinary storm. It will not die down of itself. It was sent by Kotura, the Master of the Winds. He must be angry at us. He wants us to send him a good wife."

He turned to his eldest daughter and said:

"You must go to Kotura, my daughter, or our people will perish. Go, and be his wife, and beg him to stop the storm!"

"How can I go?" asked the girl. "I don't know the way!"

"I will give you a little sled. Push it against the wind, and follow it wherever it goes. The wind will loosen the lacing of your clothes—don't stop to tie it. Snow will get into your boots—don't stop to shake it out. You will come to a high mountain. Climb up to the top. There you will stop and shake the snow out of your boots and tie the laces. When you are on the mountaintop, a little bird will fly up to you. It will alight on your shoulder. Don't drive it away—stroke and pet it tenderly. Then sit down in the sled and slide downhill. The sled will bring you right to the entrance of Kotura's tent. Go in, but don't touch anything, just sit down and wait. When Kotura comes, do everything he tells you."

The eldest daughter dressed, stepped behind the sled, and pushed it against the wind.

After she walked a little, the laces on her clothing loosened and she began to feel cold. She did not obey her father and stopped to tie them. Snow got into her boots. She stopped to shake it out. Then she went on, walking in the face of the storm. She came to a mountain and climbed up. A little bird flew up to her and wanted to settle on her shoulder. But the girl waved her hands and drove it off. The bird circled around a little, and flew away. The old man's daughter sat down in the sled and slid downhill. The sled stopped near a large tent.

The girl entered the tent and saw some roast venison lying there. She made the fire, warmed herself, and began to eat the meat, pulling off the fattest pieces. She had a good meal and began to wait. Soon she heard someone approach the tent. The skin over the entrance was raised, and a young giant came in. It was Kotura himself. He looked at the girl and asked:

"Where did you come from? What brings you here?"

"My father sent me to you."

"What for?"

"To be your wife."

"Get up, then, and cook the meat I have brought from the hunt."

The girl cooked the meat.

Kotura told her to take the meat from the pot and divide it in half.

"One half," he said, "will be for us. Put the other half in that bowl and take it to the next tent. Do not enter the tent, but wait by the door. An old woman will come out. Give her the meat and wait until she returns the bowl."

The girl took the meat and went out of the tent. The blizzard raged, the snow was whirling and flying, and she could not see anything. How could anybody find the way in such a storm? The girl walked a little to the side. Then she stopped, thought a while, and threw the meat out into the snow. After that she returned to Kotura with an empty bowl.

Kotura glanced at her and asked:

"Did you take the meat where I told you?"

"I did."

"Show me the bowl, I want to see what they gave you for the meat."

The girl showed him the empty bowl. Kotura did not say anything. He ate and went to bed.

In the morning he brought some raw deerskins to the tent and told her:

"While I am out hunting, dress these skins and make me new clothes, new boots, and mittens. When I come back, I shall see how skillful you are."

Kotura went away into the tundra, and the old man's daughter sat down to work. Suddenly the skin over the entrance was lifted and a gray-haired old woman came in.

"Girl," she said, "there is something in my eye. Help me to get it out!"

"Don't bother me, I'm working," said the girl. "I have no time."

The woman said nothing, turned, and went away. The old man's daughter remained alone in the tent. She scraped and kneaded the skins, cut them out with a knife, and hurried to make the clothes for Kotura. She stitched the pieces together quickly, any old way. How could she sew them well in a single day? Besides, she did not even have the proper needle and thread to sew them with.

In the evening Kotura came home from the hunt and asked her:

"Are my clothes ready?"

"They are."

Kotura felt them with his hand. The skins were stiff and badly finished. The stitching was crooked. The parts did not fit together. And everything was too narrow. Kotura became very angry and threw the old man's daughter out of the tent into a deep snowdrift, and left her there to freeze.

And the storm raged and howled still more fiercely.

The old man sat in his shabby tent, listening to the wailing wind which blew night and day, and said:

"My eldest daughter did not heed my words. She did not do as I told her! This is why the storm will not abate. Kotura is angry."

And he turned to his middle daughter:

"Now you will have to go. Get yourself ready."

The old man made a little sled, gave his middle daughter the same instructions, and sent her off to Kotura. Then he went back to his tent and sat down by the fire with his youngest daughter, waiting for the storm to die down.

The middle daughter pushed the sled against the wind. On the way her laces got untied, her boots were filled with snow. She felt cold and forgot her father's warning. She stopped and shook out her boots, and tied the lacing.

On top of the mountain she saw the little bird. She waved her hands and drove it away. Then she sat down on the sled and tobogganed downhill, right to Kotura's tent.

She came into the tent, made a fire, ate her fill of

venison, and began to wait for Kotura.

After a while Kotura returned from hunting, saw the girl and asked:

"What brings you to me?"

"My father sent me."

"What for?"

"To be your wife!"

"Then why do you sit there? I am hungry. Hurry up and cook me some meat for dinner!"

When the meat was ready, Kotura told the girl to take it from the kettle and divide it in half.

"One half will be for us," said Kotura. "Put the other half into a bowl and take it to the next tent. Don't enter the tent, but wait until the bowl is returned to you."

The girl took the meat and went out of the tent. The blizzard raged, blasts of snow whirled around her, she could not see anything. She did not want to go any farther. She threw the meat into the snow, stood a while, and came back to Kotura.

"Did you take the meat where I told you?" asked Kotura.

"I did."

"You were very fast about it! Show me the bowl; I want to see what they gave you for the meat."

He glanced at the empty bowl, did not say anything, and went to bed. In the morning he brought some raw deerskins into the tent and told the girl to make new clothes for him by evening.

"Go to work. In the evening I shall see how skillful you are."

He went off to hunt, and the girl sat down to her sewing, in a hurry to finish her task by evening. Suddenly a gray-haired old woman came into the tent.

"Girl," she said, "something got into my eye. Help me to get it out! I cannot do it myself."

"I have no time to bother with your eye! I have enough to do as it is. Go away, don't disturb me!"

The old woman did not say anything. She turned and left the tent. In the evening Kotura came back from the hunt and asked:

"Are my new clothes ready?"

"They are."

"Let me try them on."

He began to try them on. The skins were badly cut, all the stitching was crooked, and everything was too wide. Kotura became angry and threw the old man's second daughter into the same snowdrift with her elder sister.

The old man, meantime, sat with his youngest daughter in their tent, waiting and waiting for quiet weather. But the storm grew worse, the wind became more and more violent, as if it wanted to carry away the tents.

"My daughters did not listen to my words!" said the old man. "They made it even worse, they angered Kotura. You are my last daughter, but there is nothing I can do, I must send you to Kotura to be his wife. If I don't, our people will perish of hunger. Prepare for the journey."

The old man told his last daughter how to get to Kotura and what to do when she came there.

The girl went out of the tent, stepped behind the sled, and rolled it in the face of the blizzard. The wind howled and roared, blinding her with the driven snow, almost blowing her off her feet. She could not see her way, but she struggled through the storm, remembering every word of her father's instructions, doing everything just as he told her. The lacing on her clothes got loose, but she did not stop to tie it. Snow got into her boots, but she did not shake it out. She felt cold and moved with difficulty against the wind, but she did not stop, pushing on and on.

She came to a mountain and climbed to the top. There she halted, shook the snow out of her boots, and tied the lacing on her clothes. A little bird flew up to her and alighted on her shoulder. The girl did not chase it away. She stroked its feathers and warmed it in her hands. The bird flew away, and the girl sat down in the sled and coasted downhill, straight to Kotura's tent.

She went in and sat down to wait for him. Suddenly the skin was lifted over the entrance and a young giant stepped into the tent. Seeing the girl, he laughed and asked:

"What brings you to me?"

"My father sent me."

"What for?"

"To ask you to stop the storm, or all the people in our camp will perish!"

"Then why are you sitting there? Why don't you make a fire and cook the meat? I am hungry, and I see that you have eaten nothing either since you came."

The girl quickly cooked the meat, took it out of the kettle and served it to Kotura. They ate half of it, and he told her to take the rest to the next tent.

The girl took the bowl with the meat and went out. The blizzard roared, sweeping and whirling great gusts of snow worse than before. Where could she go? How could she find the tent? She stood for a while, thinking, then she went on.

She walked, without knowing the direction. Suddenly the bird appeared again and started flitting around her. Then it flew in a straight line, and the girl followed it. Wherever the bird flew, there she went, until she saw a spark flash nearby. She went toward the spark, thinking it was the tent. But when she came nearer, she found no tent, only a mound of snow, with a little coil of smoke rising from it. The girl walked all around it, then she pushed with her foot, and an entranceway opened. A gray-haired old woman looked out and asked:

"Who are you? Why have you come here?"

"I've come to bring you some meat, Grandma. Kotura told me to give it to you."

"Kotura told you? Very well, then, let me have it. And wait a while outside."

The girl stood by the mound, waiting. She waited for a long time. At last the entranceway opened again. The old woman looked out and gave her the bowl, filled with something. The girl returned to Kotura.

"Why did it take you so long?" asked Kotura. "Did you find the tent?"

"I did."

"Did you take the meat there?"

"I did."

"Where is the bowl? I want to see what's in it."

Kotura looked. The bowl was filled with knives, scrapers, tools for pounding and softening deerskins, and steel needles.

Kotura laughed. "They gave you many things! You'll find them useful!"

In the morning Kotura got up, brought raw deerskins into the tent, and told the girl to make him new clothes, boots, and mittens by evening.

"If you do a good job, I'll take you as my wife!"

Kotura left, and the girl set herself to work. The old woman's presents were just what she needed: She had everything necessary for making clothes. But how much can be done in a single day? However, she did not stop to think, but worked as best she could, kneading the skins, scraping and pounding them till they were soft, busily cutting and sewing. Suddenly the skin over the doorway was lifted and a gray-haired old woman came into the tent. The girl recognized her. It was the woman to whom she had brought the meat the night before.

"Help me, girl," said the old woman. "Take out the speck of dust that got into my eye. I cannot do it myself."

The girl did not refuse her. She put aside her work and tried to remove the speck of dust.

"Good," said the old woman. "My eye does not hurt any more. Now, take a look in my right ear!"

The girl looked into her ear and jumped with fright.

"What did you see there?" asked the old woman.

"There is a young woman sitting in your ear."

"Why don't you call her? She'll help you make Kotura's clothes."

The old man's daughter was happy to have help. She called the girl. In answer to her call, four girls leaped out of the woman's ear, and all four set them-

selves to work, kneading and pounding the skins, scraping, cutting, and sewing. All the clothes were ready long before evening. Then the old woman hid the girls back in her ear and left.

In the evening Kotura came from the hunt and asked:

"Did you make everything I told you?"

"I did."

"Well, let me see it, let me try it on!"

Kotura picked up the clothes and felt them. The skins were soft and velvety. He tried them on. They were neither wide, nor narrow. Everything was cut well, the pieces were sewn together properly, the stitching was neat and strong. Kotura smiled and said:

"I like you! And my mother and four sisters like you, too. You work well, and you are brave; you went out in the face of the raging storm to save your people. Be my wife! Stay here and live with me in my tent."

And as soon as he said it, the storm over the tundra died down. People no longer had to hide and freeze in their tents. Everyone came out. The men went hunting, and in the evening the fires were lit in all the tents and the families gathered around them for their supper, happy that the Master of the Winds was no longer angry at humankind.

THE MISTRESS OF FIRE

A Selkup Tale

hey say it happened very long ago, in the encampment where seven families lived in seven tents.

One day the men prepared for the hunt and set out. Only women and children were left in the camp.

For three days everything went well. But in the evening of the third day things went amiss. In one of the tents a woman was cooking her dinner. She piled up wood in the fire, hung a kettle with venison over it, and sat down by the hearth with her baby on her knees to wait for the meat to get ready. The child laughed, and the woman smiled.

Suddenly a log cracked and sparks flew from the hearth. One spark burned the child's hand and he began to cry. The woman reproached the fire:

"What do you think you are doing? I feed you wood, I tend you, and you hurt my child!"

The baby was frightened by his mother's scolding and cried still louder. The woman carried him back and forth in the tent and rocked him in her arms, but he would not quiet down. Angered, the woman slapped the child, and he began to scream so hard that he could not catch his breath. The woman should have blamed herself, but she was angry at the fire instead.

"See what you've done!" she shouted. "I'll give you no more wood, I'll chop you up, I'll drown you in water!"

She put the baby in his cradle, snatched up an axe and began to chop away at the fire. Then she took a pitcher of water and splashed it on the hearth. The fire hissed and went out.

The woman said:

"Now you'll know how to hurt my son! Not a spark, not a live bit of flame is left of you!"

There was no fire. It became cold and dark in the tent. The child began to cry again.

The woman bethought herself. She bent over the hearth and raked the ashes to find a live coal. But she herself had said she would not leave a single spark. And she hadn't.

And the boy kept crying. The mother said to herself:

"I'll run over to the next tent and get some fire for my hearth."

She ran over. But as soon as she entered her neighbor's tent, the flames in the fireplace sputtered and began to die down. The last blue tongue of flame sent up a coil of smoke and disappeared.

The woman ran to her other neighbors. But the moment she would open the door, the fire would go out. She did not even have to enter, only to open the door. She went to almost every tent in the camp, and everywhere she came, the fire died. Only in one last tent was it still burning.

That tent belonged to an old woman who had seen much in her lifetime, and knew much. The woman stood a while before the tent, afraid to enter. But what was she to do? Her little son might freeze to death unless she got some fire. And she went in.

The fire in the hearth fluttered, smoked, and went out. The woman cried. And the old woman raked the ashes, looking for a spark or a live coal. She found none. The hearth was dark and cold.

"I have never seen anything like it," said the old woman. "I tend my fire, I feed it well. When I go to sleep, I cover the live coals with ash. Why did the fire go out? Have you done something wrong, you cold frog? Have you insulted the fire in your hearth?"

The woman hung her head and was silent.

"I see you have," said the old woman. "What's to be done now? Let us go to your tent and see."

They went out together and walked through the camp. Every tent was quiet and dark, as though all people had abandoned their homes, as though the entire camp had died out.

In the woman's tent the child had cried so much he had no strength left to cry any more. The old woman took a piece of dry wood and tried to make a fire. She worked a long time, but nothing came of it. The fire would not start.

The old woman dropped her weary arms and said to the woman again:

"The fire in the hearth is sacred, it gives us all life. It feeds us and it lights our homes. When the fire goes out it is as if the sun went out. We shall freeze, we shall die, it will be the end of our people."

The old woman got down on her knees and saw the Mistress of Fire sitting in the corner of the fireplace. Her clothing was ash-gray and her skin glowed like a coal faintly covered with ash.

The Mistress of Fire rocked back and forth, then she said to the old woman:

"You are wasting your efforts! There shall be no fire for you. The woman offended me grievously. She chopped my face with an axe, she blinded me with water, she screamed evil words at me!"

The old woman began to plead:

"Don't be angry, Mistress of Fire! Take pity on us! This stupid woman is to blame, but the others are innocent."

But the Mistress of Fire shook her head, and her hair floated like bluish smoke around it.

The old woman pleaded again:

"Tell us what to do to make the fire burn again in our tents. We shall do everything you say."

The Mistress of Fire replied:

"There are no words, there is no power in the world that can make the fire burn as before. Even I do not have those words or that power. Now the fire can be lit only with the heat of a human heart."

The young woman sat, pressing her child to her breast and crying.

And the old woman said to her:

"You see what you have done? All seven human tribes must perish because of you. Hunters, brave as angry bears and strong as elk, must perish. Diligent women will wither over cold hearths. Small children will die, and old men, and old women. For there is no life without fire."

The woman's tears dried. She rose and gave her child to the old woman, and said:

"Take good care of him!"

Then she threw herself on the stones of the hearth. The Mistress of Fire touched a finger to her breast. And all at once the fire flared up. It roared and raged in the hearth. And the old woman saw how the Mistress of Fire caught the woman into her fiery arms and carried her away in a shower of sparks through the opening in the roof of the tent.

And the old woman said:

"This is the birth of the tale of how a fire was lit by a living heart. The Selkups will remember forever what happened in our camp today. They will guard and cherish the fire in their tents!"

A LONG NIGHT'S SLEEP

A Ket Tale

his happened a long time ago. One day two Kets went out into the woods to hunt, just after the first snow had fallen. They shot squirrels, they tracked sable, they set out traps for ermine. They were deep in the taiga before they noticed that it was getting dark.

"We'll have to spend the night in the woods," said one of the hunters.

"Why not?" the second answered. "We'll sleep by the fire."

They went off in different directions to gather firewood.

"Hey!" cried one. "There is a bear's den here!"

"And the bear?" shouted the other.

"The bear is gone. He must have wandered off to another place."

"All right, I'll come right over."

They made a fire near the entrance to the lair, drank a kettle of tea which they had brought from home, and ate.

The first hunter looked up into the sky and said:

"There will be a blizzard tonight!"

And the second one answered:

"That's right! The moon is hidden behind clouds, and the wind is rising."

They crawled into the lair. It was soft there, with dry grass on the ground, as though the bear had made it ready for them. To make sure they would not be cold during the night they stuffed the entrance with one hunter's fur jacket, and covered themselves with the other jacket. Now neither wind nor snow could frighten them.

"This bear," they said, "is a good man. May he be warm in his new house too!"

They were snug and comfortable, and soon they fell asleep. And they slept.

Then all at once they awakened. They lay and listened.

"The storm is not howling any more. It must have quieted down by morning," said one.

"There must be lots of snow. Look at the bright light coming through the cracks."

They crawled out of the lair, stood up, and looked around.

"How can this be?" said one. "Something is wrong. The sun has the winter and summer mixed up. Look how high it has climbed in the sky."

"And all the snow has melted in a single morning," answered the other. "I have never seen anything like it! Hurry up, let's go home."

They came to the camp. The dogs barked wildly at them and would not stop.

"Something is strange," said the first hunter. "Our own dogs do not recognize us."

Two children ran out of two tents to see why the dogs were barking.

"Are these our children?" wondered the second hunter. "They look like ours, but haven't they grown too much in a single night?"

The children looked at them and ran back into their tents. Instead of them, the hunters' wives came out. They clapped their hands and laughed, and cried. Then other people came running. They began to question the hunters: where had they been so long? How had they kept from freezing and starving to death?

The hunters looked at each other, and suddenly they understood it all. They had slept in the lair not a night, but the whole winter long, from autumn to spring!

But how could that have happened? Well, that's how. A guest does as his host does. And those two hunters climbed into a bear's home. And so they slept, like bears, all winter.

This may be a true story, or it may not. But ever since then no Ket will sleep in a bear's lair. Who wants to sleep all through the winter? What hunter wants to lose a winter's catch?

THE CRANE'S FEATHER

A Yakut Tale

eople tell, people sing about the brave hunter Yudjian; they tell, they sing about his little brother Hodjugur, about their lives and the events that befell them.

The two brothers lived without a mother and without a father. The older brother was both father and mother to the younger. And this is how they lived: when the sun had barely lifted its edge over the earth, the older brother, Yudjian, would already be out hunting in the woods. When the sun rose higher, the younger brother, Hodjugur, would get up, sweep the yard, feed the horses and the cows. In the evening, he would start a fire in the fireplace, and by then Yudjian would be back from the hunt.

Yudjian was a brave and skillful hunter. Before

59

dawn, he drove fur animals from their lairs. At dawn, he chased the elk. At sunset, he wrestled with the bear. And his arrows never missed a wolf. In the brothers' yurt there were many soft skins, and fat and meat were always plentiful.

One day, as always, Yudjian went out to hunt. Young Hodjugur, as always, remained at home. He went out of the yurt to sweep the yard and heard a honking in the sky. He looked up. Seven white cranes were circling over him. On the side of the sun, their wings glowed warmly pink. In the shadow they turned a delicate pale blue. Hodjugur waved his hand to the cranes, and they came lower.

"Is anyone else at home-home?" they asked.

"I am home alone-alone," he answered. "My older brother is out hunting."

The cranes asked one another:

"Shall we play for a while with the boy, sisters? He won't be lonely, and we shall have some fun, too."

They came down into the yard, walked all around it on their long legs, then threw off their white-feathered skins and turned into beautiful maidens. They started merry games with Hodjugur. They raced, played hide and seek, danced, and sang. They ran into the yurt and looked at everything. All day they played and laughed. When the sun began to set they hurriedly put on their white-feathered skins, turned back into cranes, flapped their wings, and took off.

Soon Yudjian returned with the day's catch.

He looked around—the yard had not been swept, the hungry cows lowed in the barn, the thirsty horses neighed in the stable. The wood had not been chopped, water had not been brought, the fire had not been started.

"Why haven't you done your day's work?" he asked Hodjugur.

"I'm sorry-sorry, older brother!" said Hodjugur. "I slept all day, I thought the sunset was the dawn."

The older brother laughed and was not angry. Together they quickly finished the chores. They fed the cows, watered the horses, and cooked their own food. After eating, they went to bed.

The next morning, as soon as his brother was out of the yard, Hodjugur jumped up. He did not idle the hours away on the soft skins. He ran out of the yurt and looked up at the sky. And the cranes were already there, circling over him, beneath the sky, above the yard.

"He is gone! My brother is gone!" Hodjugur cried to them. "Come down, hurry!"

The cranes came down and turned into maidens. And they played the same games as the day before. Again Hodjugur did not notice how the day went by. In parting, the cranes said to him:

"Don't tell your brother about us. If you say a single word, we shall not come back!"

They flew away. Like large snowflakes they melted in the sky. And Hodjugur hurried to catch up with his chores. But his brother was already on the way home, leading an elk by his nostrils.

Yudjian looked around and saw again that nothing had been done. This time he was angry.

"Will you tell me that you overslept again?"

"I will," said Hodjugur.

Yudjian gave Hodjugur a thrashing, not in anger, but to teach him a lesson. But to himself he thought: something is behind it, there must be a reason for this. The boy was never lazy before, he did everything that needed to be done with good will.

In the morning, Yudjian rose as usual. He took his bow and arrows, left the yurt, but did not go into the woods. He threw himself upon the ground and turned into a flea. Then he hid in a crack in the fence and waited.

Ah-h, Hodjugur was not asleep at all, he was not idling in his furry bed. He ran out of the yurt, stopped in the middle of the yard next to the hitching post, and raised his head. The flea thrust out its head and looked up too. A flock of cranes was circling in the sky, saying human words in their own cry:

"Hey, little Hodjugur, is your brother gone?"

"He's gone, he's gone!" cried Hodjugur, gaily waving his arms. "Come down, come down, hurry!"

But the cranes would not come down.

"Why is your yard darkened by shadow? Why is your yurt, why is your fire hidden by a dark fog?"

"It only seems so to you," answered Hodjugur. "The sun has not yet risen very high. You can see it from up above, but it has not come here as yet."

"So your brother is not home?" the cranes asked once again.

"No, no! He has already reached the woods and found his quarry, he is already tracking it!"

Seven white cranes came down into the yard. They turned into maidens and hung their feathered skins on the hitching post.

Yudjian stared at them as though bewitched. Each one was beautiful, but the seventh was the loveliest of them all. The crane girls raced one another, but she was the fastest of all. They danced, but she had the lightest step of all, as if her feet never touched the ground. And Hodjugur stayed closest to her, as if she were his favorite companion.

The day began to turn into evening, and the maidens said to Hodjugur:

"Your brother will come home soon, it is time for us to go."

And Yudjian sat in his crack, thinking:

My brother spoke the truth. I have not noticed either how the day ran into evening. It is like a marvelous dream!

The maidens hurried to the hitching post and stretched their hands to get their skins. But the flea had hopped out of its hiding place and got there first. And Yudjian turned back into himself and seized the skin of the seventh maiden.

Six white cranes rose up into the sky. One girl sobbed on the ground, begging the hunter to return her skin. But Yudjian said:

"I looked at you all day, rejoicing in your beauty. Now take a look at me. If I don't please you, take the skin and fly wherever you will. But if I do, stay here and be my wife."

The maiden looked at him through her tears. Her tears dried and she smiled at him.

"I will stay," she said quietly.

Yudjian asked:

"What shall I do with the skin? Shall I hang it on a pole in the yurt, or burn it in the fireplace?"

The maiden turned white like newly fallen snow.

"Don't throw it into the fire! If you do, misfortune will befall me. And do not hang it in the yurt. On a spring day I may be overcome with sudden longing for the sky and forget everything on earth. I will not pity you, I will not pity myself, I will fly away and away! Hide it so that no one's hands will touch it, no one's eyes will see it."

Yudjian hid the white-feathered skin in a chest bound with iron. He locked the chest with three locks, and hung the keys high on a peg by the door.

And Yudjian and the maiden lived happily as man and wife. As soon as they awakened, they spoke kind words of greeting to each other. In the morning the wife prepared her husband's hunting gear and wept as though he were leaving her forever. In the evening Yudjian hurried home as though he had not seen his wife for a whole year.

The yurt was always clean and tidy. A welcoming fire burned always in the hearth, the animals were fed and watered, the yard was swept.

One thing was bad: Hodjugur had gotten altogether spoiled and out of hand. In the past, he had all the household chores to do, but now the young wife did everything. And all day long the boy ran about wild, forever thinking up new mischief. The autumn passed, the winter went by.

One day the young woman went out for water. She came down to the river and forgot what she had come for. The clear sky turned the water blue, the songbirds were building their nests. Everything was in bloom. For a long time she stood motionless. Then she shook herself, filled her vessel with water, and turned homeward.

But while she was away, the boy Hodjugur was in the yurt, looking high and low for his brother's old bow and arrow. He had long wanted to become a hunter, to help his brother, but Yudjian kept telling him that he was still too young and did not know how to use a bow and arrow. And Hodjugur decided that it was time for him to learn. If he could find the bow and arrows, he would practice in secret and surprise his brother.

Hodjugur turned everything in the yurt upside down, but could not find what he was looking for.

Could they be in the chest? he wondered.

He took the three keys from the peg, unlocked the three locks, and raised the heavy lid. He did not find the bow and arrows, but he found the white-feathered crane skin. He took it out and admired it: such pretty feathers!

At this moment his sister-in-law came in. She stopped still and looked.

"Give me the skin," she said.

Her voice did not seem to be her own, it sounded like the honking of cranes, far, far away.

Hodjugur hid the skin behind his back.

"I will not give it to you," he said. "Yudjian had good reason to lock it in the chest. I found it by chance, and I will put it back at once."

"Just let me hold it for a moment," the woman begged. "I will give you my golden earrings."

"I am not a girl! What do I need your golden earrings for?"

"I will give you a belt embroidered with silver."

"A man does not need a woman's belt."

"I will give you a knife with a carved handle, with an inlaid sheath."

Hodjugur's eyes glittered.

"A knife is a fine thing for a hunter!" said the boy. "Let me have it!"

He seized the knife and gave her the skin.

She threw it over her shoulders and turned into a white crane. She went out into the yard, stepping carefully on her long legs, afraid to spread her wings, afraid they would lift her from the ground and carry her off into the sky. Yudjian would miss her, and she herself would sicken with longing for him.

She was just going to take off the skin when she heard cranes calling. Six cranes were circling above the yard, calling her to join them. She leaped up with a sorrowful cry and spread her wide wings.

Hodjugur ran out when he heard her. Frightened,

he ran after her and tried to catch her by the wing, but he was too late. The crane rose up, and only a single feather remained in his hand.

Seven cranes circled over the yurt for the last time. Then they rose and rose, higher and higher, until they disappeared behind a cloud.

Hodjugur followed them with his eyes, then he shook his head and said:

"And she only asked to hold it in her hands for a moment! Never again will I believe a woman!"

He sat down in the middle of the yard, put down the feather next to him, and began to play with the knife. And this was how his brother, who returned from hunting earlier than usual, found him.

"Where did you get the knife?" he asked.

"Your wife gave it to me."

"And where is this feather from?"

Hodjugur was silent. His brother shook him by the shoulders, he knew that some misfortune had occurred.

And Hodjugur began to cry.

"I found the skin by chance. Your wife asked me to let her hold it in her hands for a moment. Then she put it on and flew away. The cranes were calling her."

Yudjian had never struck his brother in anger. But

now Hodjugur learned for the first time how terrible his brother's anger could be. Yudjian beat him with a heavy, braided whip, he called him a dog. At last, his anger quenched, he pushed Hodjugur away, ran to the stable, led out his finest horse, and mounted him. The reddish-golden horse, with a bright mane and tail, danced under him. Without a look at his brother, Yudjian rode out of the yard. But before he left, he picked up the white feather from the ground.

Yudjian galloped on the golden horse, the reins in one hand, the white feather in the other. The feather turned of itself, pointing the way.

It was a long ride. Yudjian crossed rivers, rode around lakes, tore through dense woods, galloped over plains. He slept under the open sky, shielded from the wind by the horse's wide back. He lost the count of days and nights.

At last he reached the foot of a high mountain. The feather rose, its sharp end pointing upward. Yudjian left his horse to graze in the green pasture and began to climb. The mountainside was steep. The first day Yudjian climbed only one quarter of the way. On the second day he reached the midpoint. Then, with renewed strength, for he saw a white yurt at the summit, he climbed on. The cliffs were ever steeper, ever more forbidding, the gorges ever wider, the rocks ever sharper. For yet another day he climbed and climbed, but in the end he reached the top and entered the white yurt.

Splendid skins covered the walls of the yurt. A merry fire gleamed in the fireplace. In the middle stood a golden cradle, and a Chichah-bird was rocking it. Seeing the man, the bird shook his wings and cried "Cheep-chi-chip!" Then in a human voice he asked:

"Is your name Yudjian? Is it your wife you are searching for?"

"Yudjian is my name. And I am searching for my wife," he answered, his eyes never leaving the cradle.

"Well, then," said the bird, "come and look at your son."

Yudjian bent over the cradle and saw a beautiful child. The child stretched his arms to his father.

"Chee-chip!" said the bird. "The part seeks the whole, the little drop of blood longs for its own blood. Play with your child, Yudjian, I am tired of rocking the cradle."

Yudjian turned himself into a white ermine, ran up and down the cradle, jumped, and tumbled. And the boy laughed.

Light steps were heard, and the door creaked. The bird said:

"I do not know whether your wife will want to see you. Hide quickly!"

The ermine-Yudjian hid behind the skins. And the child began to cry without his playmate. A white crane ran into the yurt, threw off her skin, and the young mother hurried to the cradle. She took the child into her arms. He felt her warmth and grew quiet.

The ermine came out from behind the furs and turned back into Yudjian. He seized the feathered skin and threw it into the fire. The mother turned with a cry. Reproachfully, she whispered to her husband:

"Why, why did you do it?"

And she fell dead at his side.

Yudjian caught her in his arms, pressed her to his breast, tried to warm her with his breath, to bring her back to life. But the woman was motionless, sunk into the sleep of death. Yudjian laid her on the skins and bowed his head.

"This is my blackest day! My time of grief has come! She warned me, and I did not heed her warnings. I gave way to my violent heart, my hasty hand! She said misfortune would come of burning her skin —and now misfortune is here! I alone am to blame. I will redeem my guilt, I will make up for my rashness by patience and cunning. I will conquer weakness with strength, simplicity with guile. I will undo the harm I have done!"

Yudjian ran out of the yurt. A light cloud lingered near the mountaintop. He leaped upon it, and it floated away, swaying and billowing. They went on and on. The sun had set, the sky had darkened. The cloud swam along the great starry way. It came to a constellation and stood still.

Yudjian stepped off the cloud onto the Upper Earth. He looked around him. It was just as on the earth below—solid ground, a dwelling, a fire in the hearth.

On an eight-legged copper dais sat a young woman combing her red silken hair. Her hair was four times as long as her body, and she combed it with a golden comb and wrapped it on a silver staff. Yudjian said to her:

"Daughter of the Constellation, daughter of Master Yurgyal! Timid Shamaness Yurguk-Udagan! I have come to ask you to be my wife. Will you take me as your husband?"

The daughter of the Constellation looked at him. He was tall and handsome, and she answered quietly:

"I will."

"Then gather your clothes and your ornaments, and prepare for the journey. I shall await you on the top of the highest mountain."

The Timid Shamaness busied herself, preparing her clothes and her ornaments, gathering her dowry of cattle. And Yudjian went on.

He came to the yurt of the Master of the Moon. A young woman sat on an eight-legged copper dais, combing her silver-silk hair. Her hair was six times as long as her body, and she combed it with a golden comb, and wrapped it on a silver staff. Yudjian said to her:

"Daughter of the Master of the Moon, Shamaness of Moonlight! I have come to ask you to be my wife. Will you have me as your husband?"

The daughter of the Master of the Moon looked at him. His face shone with courage, his eyes were bright with spirit. And she said:

"I will. But give me time to get my dowry together."

"I have no time to wait," said Yudjian. "Do everything you need to do according to your own knowledge. Then come to me on the highest mountain. I shall await you there."

The daughter of the Master of the Moon, the Shamaness of Moonlight, busied herself, gathering her clothes and her adornments, calling together her dowry of cattle. And Yudjian went on.

While he walked, the night ended. In the distance

gleamed the yurt of the Master of the Sun. Yudjian walked straight toward it.

Near the shining yurt, on an eight-legged copper dais sat a young woman, combing her sunny-silken hair. Her hair was eight times as long as her body, and she combed it with a golden comb, and wrapped it on a silver staff. Yudjian said to her:

"Daughter of the Master of the Sun! Shamaness Kugyal-Udagan! I have come to you to take you as my wife if you will have me as your husband!"

The Shamaness Kugyal-Udagan could look at the blazing face of her father, the Master of the Sun, without blinking. But now she shut her eyes, dazzled with love for him who had come to woo her. And she said to Yudjian:

"I will. Why not?"

Yudjian told her also to come to him on the highest mountain when she was ready.

The Shamaness Kugyal-Udagan remained to prepare her dowry, and Yudjian hastened on.

He came to the edge of the Upper Earth, leaped onto the cloud that was waiting for him, and started on his return journey. He floated up to the mountain and stepped off the cloud.

In the yurt the Chichah-bird rocked Yudjian's child, and on the furs lay Yudjian's dead wife. Yudjian quickly dressed her in his own clothes, gathered up her long hair and hid it under his hat. He brought her out of the yurt, laid her before the entrance, and hid behind the yurt.

Just as he finished, his three brides came riding on their horses from three directions. Each brought a rich dowry: dresses trimmed with braid, rare furs. Each had fifty herds of horses and ninety herds of cows. The whole mountainside was covered with the herds.

The brides dismounted and saw one another.

"Friends-sisters," they said, "so all three of us shall be the wives of the same husband. Well, we shall not be bored on Earth. But where is our husband? Why is he not here to welcome us? Let us go into the yurt. He may be sleeping."

They walked with cloud-light heavenly steps toward the yurt. Then suddenly they stopped. One said:

"Oh, my sisters! I fear there is a dead man lying here!"

The second one said:

"Can it be our husband?"

The third one looked:

"It is he! It is he! He came to woo me in these clothes!"

The daughter of the Master of the Sun, Kugyal-Udagan, asked:

"Daughter of Master Yurgyal, Timid Shamaness, can you revive a dead man?"

"If I said I can, it would be untrue. And if I said I cannot, it would be untrue," replied the Timid Shamaness. "I can revive a dead man so that he becomes as one lying unconscious."

"This is not much, and it is not little," said the daughter of the Master of the Sun. Then she asked the daughter of the Master of the Moon:

"And how great is your skill, Shamaness of Moonlight?"

"I can revive a dead man so that he becomes as one profoundly asleep," she answered.

"And I," said Kugyal-Udagan, daughter of the Master of the Sun, "can return a dead man to consciousness. I can awaken him from mortal sleep."

"Well, sisters!" said all three. "Let us do our work, let us bring our husband back to life."

The Timid Shamaness, daughter of the Constellation, was the first to leap across the body. Its breast stirred, its breath blew faintly from the lips.

The Shamaness of Moonlight was second to leap across the body. Color returned to the pale face, the eyelashes quivered.

And now Kugyal-Udagan, the daughter of the Master of the Sun, stepped forward. She leaped across the body, and the dead arose. The hat slipped down, and the long hair scattered on the shoulders.

"Oh, sisters, it seems we have revived the wrong one! This is not our husband, it is a strange woman!"

And Yudjian, who was hiding behind the yurt, had heard and seen everything. He ran out and embraced his beloved wife. She hid her face on his broad chest, flushing with joy.

The shamanesses watched and looked at one another. Suddenly the child cried in the yurt. The beautiful woman who had been brought to life heard it and broke away from her husband to run to her child. And Yudjian followed her.

"There is nothing for us to do here, sisters," said the daughter of the Master of the Sun. "Our bridegroom already has a wife and child. And it is not meet for us, heavenly shamanesses, to be junior wives, second to a woman of Earth! Let us return home."

She jumped upon her horse, the horse rose up and galloped straight into the sky. The two others followed her. On the way the daughter of Yurgyal, the Timid Shamaness, cried:

"Oh, sisters, what have we done? We have forgotten our dowries back on Earth!"

But Kugyal-Udagan, daughter of the Master of the Sun, laughed proudly.

"My father has more wealth than the few miserable herds I left below," she said. "He will not mind the loss. If I need more, he'll give me all I want."

"Nor will my father reproach me!" said the daughter of the Master of the Moon, the Shamaness of Moonlight.

Yurguk-Udagan, the daughter of the Constellation, flushed at these proud words.

"Let my dowry stay behind as well. My father, Master Yurgyal, is not as rich as yours, but he is as generous as they are. He too will not begrudge me anything."

And so they did not turn back. All the wealth, all three dowries, remained with Yudjian. He now prepared for the return journey. He whistled lightly, and his fiery horse came racing to him from the green valley below.

He mounted the horse, lifted up his wife before him, fastened his son's cradle at his left knee. On the edge of the cradle sat the faithful nurse, the Chichah-bird, singing songs to the boy.

Thrice fifty herds of horses ran before them. Thrice ninety herds of cows followed them.

This was how they journeyed, and this was how they came. A handsome youth, tall and broad in the shoulders, ran out to meet them.

"Is this you, Hodjugur, my younger brother?" asked Yudjian.

"Have I grown so much that you no longer recognize me?" laughed Hodjugur. "I see you found your wife, my dear sister-in-law, and brought her back. Forgive me for the trouble I have been to you!"

And they lived happily together. This is what people tell, this is what people sing about.

THE SINGING MAN

A Dolgan Tale

t the edge of the woods and the edge of the tundra there was a small log cabin. A woman lived in it with her three sons. The two elder sons were big and strong. The youngest, called Kunachi, was weak, and spent all his time lying on top of the stove. He could not walk at all, for his feet would not hold him up. Neither he nor his mother knew why he was like that. And even if she knew, she never told.

The mother was always home with Kunachi. The only time she left him was to go to the nearby woods to gather firewood. But the brothers wandered all day long in the taiga and up and down the river bank. They shot game, caught fish, and cooked their meals wherever they were. In the evening they brought home all that was left of their catch.

It was the same on the day when our tale begins. Kunachi woke for the first time at dawn, when his brothers were preparing to leave for the day's hunt. When the door closed after them, he fell asleep again. He woke a second time and heard a storm raging outside. The cabin door was wide open, all the warmth in the room had been blown away, and the stove was cold. Kunachi called his mother, but she did not answer. He wanted to climb down from his bed on the stove to close the door, but he could not and tumbled down on the floor. He hurt his side, he bruised his hand, but he crawled on all fours to the threshold.

When he got there, he raised himself on his arms and looked out. On the right he saw fallen trees, like lean, starved, angry bears, and crooked stumps, like crouching, hungry wolves.

On the left he saw his mother. She stood, holding on to the corner of the cabin, looking up. Suddenly there was a flash of lightning and a clap of thunder. Kunachi shut his eyes, and when he opened them his mother was no longer there.

"Mama, Mama!" called Kunachi.

And he heard a sound that could have been the rustling of the wind, or the voice of his mother:

"Come to me, son!"

"Where shall I come, Mama?" asked Kunachi.

But he heard nothing more. Kunachi began to cry.

With difficulty he managed to close the door, then he crawled into a corner to wait for his brothers.

In the evening the brothers returned. The house was not heated, the stove was not burning, and in the corner Kunachi lay curled up like a sick puppy.

"Why are you on the floor, Kunachi?" his brothers asked.

"I fell off the stove."

"Why is it cold in the house?"

"The wind blew open the door and blew out all the heat."

"Where is our mother?"

"I don't know."

And he told them what he had seen.

His brothers ran out of the hut, ran all around it, but found no sign and no trace of their mother. They came back and fired the stove, fed Kunachi, and went to sleep. The brothers slept, but Kunachi cried all night.

In the morning Kunachi said:

"We must go to our mother."

"But where is she?"

"She did not say."

"How can you find her if there are no traces and no footprints? Where can we look for her?"

"I may catch sight of some trace," said Kunachi. "Put me into a trough, and take me with you."

The elder brothers did as he had asked. They put Kunachi into the trough over which their mother sifted flour, tied a strong leather strap to it, and pulled their younger brother after them into the tundra, and into the woods.

The brothers walked with their eyes on the ground, but Kunachi looked all around him. It was the first time that he was out in the free, open world! In the west he saw the earth covered with bright flowers and coarse sedge, like crooked knives. In the south the mountains glowed red. In the north the snow was dazzling white.

They walked many days, spending nights in the woods, and on the thrice-third day they came to an old, dried-out lake bed, overgrown with tall grass.

"We'll stop here," said Kunachi. "The grass must be pulled up."

"What for?" asked the brothers.

"You'll find out later. Start now, and I will sleep a while."

Kunachi slept, and the brothers went to work. But they worked less than they did not work. And when Kunachi woke the tall grass stood just as it had before, with only a bare spot here and there. He said:

"You have not accomplished much. I must have slept a very short time."

"Oh, no, you slept a long time," the elder brothers

answered. "And we worked without straightening our backs. The grass is very tough, with strong roots, and we are tired."

"If you are tired, lie down and sleep a while."

The brothers stretched out on the ground and snored. When they opened their eyes, it was evening, and there was not a single blade of grass left in the dried-out lake bed. All of it had been plucked and piled up like a green mountain.

"Have you rested well?" asked Kunachi. "There is a new task waiting. I pulled up all the grass. It was not as tough as you said. But my arms are tired, and my back aches. I'll go to sleep now, and you will weave the grass into a strong, thick rope."

When Kunachi woke, he found his brothers fast asleep. Beside them lay a thin, short little rope, and the mound of grass seemed quite untouched. Kunachi sighed and went to work himself.

Who knows how long he worked, who knows how long the brothers slept, but he awakened them when there was not a single blade of grass left on the ground. The thick grass rope coiled like a snake three times around the lake bed.

The brothers were amazed and ashamed. They asked:

"Tell us what must be done now!"

"Do you see that tree? Dig it up with the roots and

bring it to me."

The brothers went to dig up the tree, but before long they returned to Kunachi.

"The trunk of this tree is very thick," they said. "The roots are deep, the branches wide. We cannot dig it out."

"Very well, then, pull my trough over to the tree."

The brothers pulled it over. Kunachi grasped the tree and bent it to the ground. He seized the lower branches, and with a heave and a tug he twisted the tree out with the roots. Then he tied the end of the rope to the treetop, lifted the tree, and threw it up into the sky. It flew and flew, with its roots up and top down, pulling the rope with it. When it reached the sky, its roots grew into it, and the rope hung down all the way to earth.

The brothers wondered. Where did the crippled, weak Kunachi get so much strength after lying in bed all his life? And Kunachi said to them:

"I have found no trace of our mother on earth. That means she is in the sky. We'll climb up the rope now."

Again the brothers wondered. Where did the crippled Kunachi who had never had a glimpse of the wide world learn so much wisdom?

The three of them began to climb. They climbed and they climbed. The brothers used their hands and feet. Kunachi could use only his hands.

At last they reached the sky. Kunachi looked around. Silver roads ran off in all directions, gleaming in the sun. But the brothers feared to raise their eyes, to see what was around them. They looked nowhere but down, at the earth from which they had come. Kunachi said to them:

"We must go now and search for our mother!"

"We will not go anywhere! We will not stir from the spot. For here, at least, we have the rope to take us back to earth."

"Well," said Kunachi, "I suppose I'll have to go myself. Perhaps my feet will carry me upon these shining roads."

He crawled up to a silver road, stepped on it, and stood up. His feet held him. He took one step, another, and walked as if he had been walking all his life. He turned and shouted to his brothers:

"Wait for me three years. If I am alive, I will return. If I am even one day late, it means I am no longer living. Then you can go back to earth. Think well of me."

"Fine! We shall wait three years," said the brothers to him. And to one another they said: "Our Kunachi is clearly not an ordinary man. And we never suspected it!"

They made a fire and sat down by it, ready to wait three years.

Kunachi walked down the silver road. He alone

knows how many days and nights he walked, but at last he came to a crossroads. He saw a little hut with silver walls and a silver roof. The hut kept turning round and round; now one side flashed, and now another. And by the hut sat a beautiful maiden. Her face was white like a summer cloud, her cheeks tender like a cloud at sunrise.

"Where are you going?" asked the maiden.

"I am looking for my mother," answered Kunachi.

"You are looking in vain," said the maiden. "What would a woman from earth be doing here? You will do better to stay with me in my hut, or else go back."

"I will not stay with you, and I will not turn back," said Kunachi. "My mother called me. I found no trace of her on earth, therefore she must be here."

"Maybe so, and maybe not," said the maiden. "The road behind you is long, the road ahead still longer. Come into the hut, have some food and take a rest."

Kunachi entered the hut. He ate what the maiden served him, rested a little, and prepared to go on.

The maiden said to him in parting:

"Your mother is not here. If you do not believe me, ask my older sister. You will come to her if you take the road that leads right."

Kunachi went to the right. He walked and walked, and once again came to a hut. Had he not measured the long road with his own feet, he would have thought that he had stood still all that time, for this hut was exactly like the first. And near it sat a maiden as beautiful as the first. But her cheeks were not delicate like a cloud at dawn; they were bright like a cloud at sunset. Her eyes shone like the earliest star in the darkening sky.

Kunachi told her where he was going, and what he was searching for.

The maiden led him into the hut, gave him food and drink, and said:

"You are not looking for your mother in vain. She is here. She was carried off by the evil Thunder, who keeps her imprisoned. If you want to free her, you must kill Thunder."

She took a sharp sword from the wall and gave it to Kunachi.

"Walk straight, don't turn off anywhere. Don't turn even if you see the Northern Lights. Stop only when you see a rider on a fast white horse. It will be Thunder, who has done you and your mother harm. He will leap down from his horse and approach you. Then you can strike him with the sword."

"He will not frighten me!" said Kunachi and went up the road.

He walked and walked, until he saw the Northern Lights playing before him, changing from red to green, from blue to yellow. Every shape could be seen in them—woods and mountains, flowery meadows, blue lakes. Kunachi looked, but did not stop.

Suddenly a rider appeared on a great white horse. Fire flashed and sparks flew from the horse's nostrils. Kunachi halted, and the rider stopped his horse, leaped down and approached him. Kunachi seized his sword as the maiden had told him and struck the rider.

Something flashed, there were rolls of thunder. Kunachi dropped the sword and fell, face down, and never remembered what happened next. Nor did he know how long he lay there. At last he opened his eyes, and saw nothing but snow all around, glittering white as far as he could see.

"I will perish here!" said Kunachi.

"You deserve it!" said a voice over the snowy plain. "You did not ask, you did not say what you wanted, you raised your sword! You obeyed the daughters of the clouds, and they deceived you."

The voice was silent. The silence was so deep that Kunachi could hear the snowflakes rustling. He stood up and tried to walk across the snow. His feet sank in the snowdrifts, and he could not walk. Someone, he thought, must want him to crawl as he had crawled for twenty years. He fell and cut his hands on the crisp coat of ice over the snow. Soon he was so exhausted, he could barely move.

"I see that I will really perish here!" Kunachi said.

"You will!" said the same voice.

Kunachi straightened up and shook his fist at the invisible being who spoke.

"I will not perish! I must find my mother. She called me, she may be in trouble."

"You shouldn't have listened to the daughters of the clouds," the voice repeated. "It is your own fault."

"But my mother did nothing wrong!" cried Kunachi.

"That is true," the voice replied. "Go, then. And we shall see if your resolve is as strong as your words."

Kunachi struggled on. After a while, there was less snow, and patches of earth began to appear here and there. His feet moved more easily now, and his heart grew light—he would surely get there!

Suddenly there was a glittering lake before him. It was so vast that he could not see the shore to the right or the left. Only straight ahead, in the far distance, there was a barely visible dark line of land. The lake was not frozen. Huge waves rolled over it, and the wind blew the foam off their crests.

Kunachi stopped. He did not know what to do. Then he said to himself:

"The road to my mother is not back, but forward. But if I walk on water, I shall drown."

He listened—perhaps the voice would advise him.

No, the voice was silent. He had to make his own decision.

"Whatever happens, I will go on!"

And then the voice said:

"Go. You will not drown."

Kunachi stepped on the water, and he did not even wet his shoe. He stepped with the other foot, and the water was firm beneath it. At every step he made, the water froze to ice. The moment he raised his foot, it melted and splashed behind him. And so Kunachi crossed the entire lake. He came out upon the shore, and a smooth silver road stretched before him.

Kunachi walked on rapidly. His feet seemed to carry him by themselves along that shining road. And again he saw the Northern Lights glimmering in the distance, red, blue, and green, ever changing, now rising like a forest, now spreading like wide rivers.

He came to the very edge of the Northern Lights, to the spot where he had first met the rider on the white horse. He halted for a moment, uncertain whether to wait or to go on. But no one was in sight, and he went on.

He did not count his steps or measure the distance he had covered. At last he came to a large house with eighty windows. He stepped across the threshold made of ten golden beams and found himself upon a golden floor. It was a handsome house, with a fine tile stove, a bench that sang, and a stove bed that told tales of olden times.

And then a woman ran out to greet him, and cried:

"Kunachi is here! My son has come here on his own two feet!"

Kunachi could not believe his eyes. Was this really his mother? She had become as beautiful as she had been as a young girl. Kunachi did not remember her like that. But he immediately recognized her loving voice.

She made her son sit down on the singing bench, and she sat down near him. They spoke about things that Kunachi knew and his mother did not know. Kunachi told her what had happened to him, what he had seen and heard, what he had done. His mother listened quietly and shook her head:

"You did a bad thing, my son! You tried to kill your own father!

"My father?" cried Kunachi.

His mother answered:

"I will tell you everything. Listen to what I say."

And she told him the things that she knew and Kunachi did not know.

It happened, she said, many years before. She wandered from place to place with her husband and two small sons. They were riding in a deer sled through the woods when a bear attacked them. He crushed her husband to death and threw himself upon her. She would have died too, but suddenly there was a peal of thunder from the clear sky, a lightning bolt flashed down and killed the bear. And a rider on a white horse appeared before her. He took care of her and her children, he did not let them perish from cold or hunger. They lived together for a year, and she gave birth to the boy Kunachi. Soon after that, Thunder, his father, began to make ready to leave. He could not remain on earth any longer, he told her. He had to return to his home in the sky. For a whole year there had been no rainstorms anywhere. This was bad for everything that grew and everything that lived. He promised to come to her whenever he could get away. And he kept his promise. He visited her three times while Kunachi was growing up, and each time he begged her to come with him. But how could she go? How could she leave her son who had been born with weak feet? On his last visit Thunder said to her: "Our son is grown now. If he loves you, he will look for you. He will come to the sky, and there I will help him. His feet will walk and never know fatigue."

The woman heeded her husband, and he carried her away. All she had time to say was, "Come to me, son!"

"I heard you," cried Kunachi. "And so I came."

"You are a good son to your mother," said the woman. "Let us wait for your father and hear what he will say."

"Where is he?"

"I don't know where he is now. He has a lot to do."

And so Kunachi lived with his mother in the big house with the eighty windows. He chopped wood for her, brought water, helped her with everything.

One day at dawn Kunachi heard the rolling of thunder. The walls shook, the golden beams rang with a golden sound. Then all was quiet. Kunachi thought:

"I must have dreamed it!"

And he fell asleep again. And when the sun was high, his mother came and said:

"Get up, son, your father has come home on his white horse. He wants to see you."

Kunachi went to see his father, Thunder, and Thunder said to him:

"You turned out to be a good son. Now make your choice: you can live here with us, or return to earth, just as you wish."

Kunachi said:

"I see that my mother is well and happy. She needs no defender. And for an earthly man it is better to live on earth. My brothers are waiting for me at the edge of the sky. I promised them to return in three years."

"You spoke true words," said Thunder. "Go, then, to your brothers. But first I will make you a gift. Choose your share of whatever I own."

There were three barns in Thunder's wide yard. Thunder led Kunachi to the first and opened the door before him.

Kunachi glanced left, and moonlight glimmered in his eyes. He glanced right, and he was dazzled by sunshine. All that brightness came from the piles of silver and piles of gold in Thunder's barn.

Kunachi shook his head.

"I need no silver, and I need no gold."

"So you do not want riches," said Thunder, and led him to the second barn.

In that barn seven-hued rainbows were piled in one corner. Lightnings flashed white and scarlet. Winds struggled to break out of leather sacks.

Kunachi shook his head again:

"No, Father, I will not take any of this, either. You will need it all yourself."

"So you do not want power," said his father. "Well, then, I will choose your gift myself. This gift is in the third barn."

Kunachi looked in and wondered. The third barn was quite empty but for a little stick that lay on the floor. The stick had three knots in it. Thunder picked it up and gave it to Kunachi with these words:

"When you feel sad, when your heart fills with longing, take out any of these knots and look into the hole. And if you are ever in trouble, this stick will always help you out."

Kunachi bid his mother and his father good-bye and set out on the return journey.

He walked fast, hurrying to his brothers. His feet never knew fatigue. Soon the Northern Lights appeared before him, shimmering with many colors. Kunachi stopped but for a moment to admire them, and hurried on. The silver road before him seemed to run by itself from under his feet.

He came to the hut. It turned and turned; now one side of it flashed, and now another. Before it sat the elder sister, the daughter of the clouds. Kunachi asked her:

"Did you know that Thunder is my father, and that my mother is his wife?"

"I knew it," she answered.

"Then why did you give me the sword, why did you lie to me? I could have killed my father and made my mother a widow!"

"Now I will tell you the truth. Thunder should not have married an earth woman. She should not live here in the sky. This is why I gave you the sword and told you to raise it against Thunder."

"My mother wishes no one any evil, and never wished you any harm."

"Maybe so," said the daughter of the clouds. "But what is done is done. Thunder will never forgive me now. Take me down to earth with you."

"Well," said Kunachi. "Come if you wish."

They walked together. Who knows how long they walked, but at last they came to the silver hut where the younger sister lived.

"Where are you going?" the younger sister asked the elder.

"Down to earth. I want to live there for a while."

"Take me with you."

And so the three of them walked on. Kunachi strode rapidly. The maidens glided on the silver road as though flying over it.

At last they came to the edge of the sky where Kunachi had left his brothers.

The brothers had already put out the fire and were preparing to go home.

"Have three years passed?" asked Kunachi.

"There are only three days left," said the brothers. "We thought you had perished, and why waste time?"

And as they spoke, they could not take their eyes away from the two maidens.

They began to climb down the rope, first the maidens, then the elder brothers. Kunachi waited for them to step down on the ground.

The maidens got there first. The brothers followed. They glanced at the maidens, then at one another. The eldest whispered to the middle one:

"Let Kunachi stay up there. Let him live in the sky. And we shall marry the maidens."

Before the middle brother had time to nod, the elder set fire to the rope. The grass rope had dried out in those three years, and the fire ran up quickly, like a yellow bird.

Kunachi was climbing down, the fire was running up. They met right in the middle, and the fire went out. Kunachi remained suspended midway between earth and sky.

He looked down. The earth was far below, but he could see his brothers running away with the maidens. Kunachi hung there and did not know what to do. The wind swayed him, the rain pelted him. Suddenly Kunachi remembered his father's present. He took the stick and held it to the end of the rope. The stick began to grow and grow, until it reached the earth, and Kunachi was able to come down.

Then the stick returned to its former size. Kunachi sat down on the grass and put the stick on his lap. He began to remember all the things that happened long ago, and the things that happened recently. Until the age of twenty, he had been fed by his brothers, who cared for him and for their mother. And now they tricked him, they plotted evil against him. They forgot everything the moment they saw the maidens. They had not even asked after their mother. They had not asked whether Kunachi found her, and how she was. The daughters of the clouds were as fickle as the clouds themselves. Kunachi did not hold any grudge against them. They had deceived him once before. But his brothers? He had trusted them as he trusted himself.

A great sadness came over him, his soul was filled with sorrow. Suddenly the stick on his knees seemed to roll over by itself. Kunachi remembered what his father had told him. He picked up the stick, took out the upper knot and looked into the hole. And at once he forgot all his sorrow. He looked and looked and could not tear his eyes away. He saw the wide tundra, the tents of the Nenets people, sleds, and deer. A multitude of tents and countless deer. The people wore embroidered clothes. They ate meat, beat their tambourines, made merry. And Kunachi himself began to feel merry and lighthearted.

He put back the top knot and took out the middle one. And he saw mountains and woods. He learned how the Khant people lived, and how the Evenks lived and hunted. How they hunted fur animals and drove their herds of deer from pasture to pasture.

They worked hard, but they also knew how to make merry. They played and laughed and wrestled near their tents. Kunachi watched, and he himself felt gay, as if he too were running races with them, lassoing deer, shooting arrows at targets.

He took out the third knot, and he saw the ageless taiga. Across it flowed the Yenisey River, wide and deep. On the river he saw rowboats and ships. On the ships there were Russians. They unloaded their goods on the shore—beautiful cloth, flour, wine. And the people who lived in the woods brought them furs in exchange. They loaded up the ships with mammoth tusks, deerskins and fox skins, ermine, and otter and squirrel. The Russians drank and treated others. They sang songs. And the ships sailed upstream and downstream. Smoke rose from their smokestacks and spread over the taiga like fog.

Kunachi watched and wondered at it all. Then he grew thoughtful. And then he started a song, telling of all he had seen.

"Well," he said to himself. "I have become a singing man! If I visit all the places I have seen I will sing even better."

He rose, slipped the stick under his arm, and set out on his journey. Who but himself can tell of all the lands that he has seen, the roads through forest and tundra he has measured with his feet, the people he has talked to, the songs he has sung!

And one day on his long singing journey he met his two brothers. They ran and never saw the earth under their feet, for now they only looked up and up. They tripped and fell, but their eyes never left the sky. And in the sky two little clouds floated away and away, and the brothers never stopped chasing them.

"I see," Kunachi said to them, "that the daughters of the clouds deceived you too."

"They did!" cried the brothers. "They left us, but they will not let us go. They beckon to us all the time and bid us follow them."

And they ran on.

Kunachi pitied them, but there was nothing he could do to help them. He followed them with his eyes a while. And he continued with his own journey.

He has lived a hundred years now. And all his life he goes from place to place, and sings his songs, and gladdens men's hearts.

UNYANY

An Evenk Tale

n a large encampment in the
North country there were many
tents covered with animal skins.
The Evenks, who lived in the
tents, were peaceful and
friendly, and they lived well.
They hunted, and they fished, and in their free time
they sang, and played, and danced.

One day they heard a loud, rushing noise in the
sky. They looked up and saw someone huge, dark,
with enormous wings. It was the evil giant, the man-
eating shaman Korendo. Korendo had a pair of wings
that he would put on to fly over the country, catching
and devouring people.

Korendo came down among the tents. He caught
the frightened people and gobbled them up, one by
one, until no one was left in the camp except a little

old woman who had hidden herself under a large iron cauldron.

Korendo never found the old woman. He swallowed everyone in sight, flapped his wings, rose high into the air, and flew away.

When the noise of his wings died down, the little old woman climbed out from under the cauldron and went from tent to tent to look for other people. But all the tents were empty. She began to cry:

"How will I live all alone?"

Then she looked into the last tent, and at first she thought that it was empty, too. She looked again, and saw a little boy, a baby, lying on a skin. The old woman was overjoyed to find another human being in the camp. She made a cradle and rocked the baby, and fed him. She called the boy Unyany.

Unyany grew not by the year, but by the day. When he got older, he began to hunt, and brought home food for himself and the old woman.

One day Unyany asked:

"Why are there only two of us in the whole camp, Granny? Only you and I? Where are our people? Did they all get sick and die?"

"No, child, they were devoured in a single night by a man-eating giant. I hid under a cauldron, and you were so little that he never noticed you in your tent. And so I fed you and brought you up."

"Where did the giant go? Tell me!"

"I'd like to tell you, but I don't know myself."

Unyany was so sad and so angry that he decided
he must find the giant and punish him. He went out
into the taiga, caught a wild deer, and brought him
to the old woman:

"Grandma, is this the giant who ate our people?"

"No, child, no! This is a good animal. It is a deer.
Take him back where you found him and let him go."

Unyany did as she told him. He took the wild deer
back to the taiga and set him free. Then he went on
to look for the man-eating giant. He caught a wolverine and dragged him home to the old woman:

"Grandma, is he the one who killed our people?"

"No, child, no! This is a wolverine. He has not done
anything wrong. Take him back where you found him
and let him go."

Unyany did as the old woman told him. He set the
wolverine free. Then he caught an elk and brought
him home:

"Grandma, is this the one who ate our people?"

"No, child! This is an elk. He does not eat people.
Take him where you caught him and let him go."

Unyany set the elk free and caught a wolf. He
brought him home and asked:

"Is this the one who ate our people?"

"No, child, it isn't. This is a wolf. Let him go!"

Unyany freed the wolf and caught a bear, but Grandma told him to free the bear as well.

And Unyany went on bringing animal after animal to the old woman—big animals and small ones. But she always told him to take them back to the taiga and let them go without hurting them.

And Unyany began to grieve—he did not know what to do to find the evil man-eater. The old woman saw his sadness, and finally she said to him:

"Child, you will not find the man-eater in the taiga! He looks like a man, but he is huge. He came here flying on wings like a bird, and he flew away—I don't know where. I only know that he was the evil shaman Korendo."

Unyany stopped wandering in the taiga. He begged the old woman to give him the lid from a large cauldron. Then he got a hammer and began to make a pair of wings for himself. All day he sat by the fire, heating the iron and hammering it. He worked day after day until he finished the wings. And he asked the old woman:

"Are these wings good enough, Grandma?"

"No, child, they are not very good. Korendo had larger ones!"

Unyany set himself to work again, making the wings larger. When they were ready, he wanted to try them out. He rose into the sky and asked the old woman:

"Grandma! I am flying as high as the black grouse! Is this how high Korendo flew?"

"No, child, he flew higher!"

Unyany worked some more. He made his wings still larger and rose into the air again, and again he asked the old woman:

"Grandma! I am flying as high as the hazel grouse! Is this how high Korendo flew?"

"No, child, Korendo flew higher! If you want to defeat him, you must fly higher than he did. You must make wings larger than his wings. Remember: Korendo is big and strong!"

Unyany did not lose heart. He did not give up, but went back to work. Without a respite, he sat by the fire, forging and hammering, building a pair of huge iron wings.

When the wings were ready, he rose into the sky to test them. He flew over the camp and asked the old woman:

"Tell me, Grandma! Did Korendo fly higher or lower than I?"

"Now you are flying higher than Korendo! He flew lower than you!"

Unyany rose to a great height and saw a huge tent in the distance. He flew toward it.

When he came to the tent, he saw Korendo's landing ground. Unyany began to circle over the tent. He circled and circled over it, singing:

"Come out, Korendo, come out of your tent!
I have come here to fight you!"

He sang for a long time, but Korendo did not come. He was not there. Instead, a woman came out of the tent. She was Korendo's wife, and she sang:

"You fool, you fool!
You cannot fight Korendo!
Korendo is a mighty shaman,
No one can vanquish him!
If you are looking for death,
Fly to Korendo!"

She pointed the direction where Unyany was to fly to find Korendo. He soared upward and flew on.

He came to a second tent and saw Korendo's landing ground. Unyany circled around the tent, singing his song, calling Korendo to battle:

"Come out, Korendo, come out of your tent!
I have come here to fight you!"

Instead of Korendo, his second wife came out of the tent and sang out in reply:

"Korendo is a mighty shaman,
  No one can vanquish him!
  If you are looking for death,
  Fly to Korendo!"

She finished her song and pointed the direction where Unyany was to fly in search of Korendo. He waved his wings and flew in that direction. He flew for a long time, until he came to a third tent and began to call Korendo. But Korendo was not there, either. Unyany flew to a fourth camp, and did not find the man-eating Korendo. Then he flew to a fifth, and did not find him. He flew to a sixth, and again he did not see Korendo, but only his sixth wife. And the sixth wife told him that Korendo was now living in the seventh camp. And, like all of Korendo's other wives, she sang him the song:

"Korendo is a mighty shaman,
  No one can vanquish him!
  If you are seeking your death,
  Fly to Korendo!"

But their words did not frighten Unyany. He flew on, to Korendo's seventh tent. He came and circled around it, singing:

"Come out, Korendo, come out of your tent!
  I have come here to fight you!"

Korendo's seventh wife heard Unyany's song. She
came out and sang in reply:

> "Do not trouble, do not call Korendo!
> He is a mighty shaman.
> I will not waken Korendo.
> He will rise on his wings,
> He will kill you!
> You are helpless and weak before him!"

But she did not frighten Unyany either. He circled
lower and lower, and sang louder and louder:

> "Korendo destroyed my people.
> I want to avenge them!
> I am small, but I do not fear him!
> Waken him quickly,
> I am ready to fight him!"

Korendo's wife went back to the tent and awakened
him. After that she came out and sang once again to
Unyany:

> "The mighty Korendo is up!
> He will put on his wings,
> And come out of the tent!
> He will fight you!"

Unyany circled right over the tent and boldly called
out:

> "Korendo! Korendo! Korendo!
> Come out to battle!"

In reply, he heard the giant's gruff voice:

> "Unyany! Unyany! Unyany!
> Wait, wait for me a while!
> I must eat before I come out!"

And Unyany sang:

> "Why should you eat, Korendo?
> You will not live much longer!
> I will avenge my people!"

Korendo replied in a gruff voice:

> "Unyany! Unyany! Unyany!
> Wait till I put on my boots!"

And Unyany sang:

> "Why do you need your boots?
> You will not live much longer!
> I will avenge my people!"

Korendo sang:

> "Unyany! Unyany! Unyany!
> Wait till I put on my wings!"

But Unyany would not leave him alone and continued to sing and to taunt him:

> "Korendo! Korendo! Korendo!
> Why do you tarry, Korendo?
> Come out, come out to fight me!
> I will avenge my people!"

Then the huge, heavy, clumsy Korendo came out of the tent, rose into the air on his wings, and rushed at Unyany. But the light and agile Unyany evaded him and quickly rose into the sky. Korendo flapped his wings, trying to rise higher than Unyany. But Unyany circled over his head, drawing him on and on.

They flew up and up for a long, long time, Unyany always just above Korendo. And, no matter how hard he tried, Korendo could not overtake Unyany and strike at him. Korendo finally began to tire, and sang out:

"Unyany! Unyany! Unyany!
Wait a while!
Come down, come down lower!
I cannot fight you at this height,
It makes my head go round!"

Unyany laughed and answered the giant:

"Korendo! Korendo! Korendo!
Why is your head going round?
What is making you dizzy?
I will not come down!
I am fighting for my people,
Avenging my brothers and sisters!
I will break, I will crush your wings!"

Unyany rushed at Korendo and circled above him, singing loudly:

"Korendo! Korendo! Korendo!
Never again will you hunt down my people
Never again will you ruin our camps!
This is your final hour!"

He threw himself upon Korendo, and smashed his wings. And the fat, clumsy Korendo dropped like a stone to the ground. His belly burst open. And all the people he swallowed came out of his belly. They went back to their camps and their tents. And never again did they have to fear Korendo. They hunted and they fished, and in their free time they sang, and played, and danced.

THE ENEMY'S TENT

A Yukagir Tale

ne evening three brothers sat in their tent. The eldest was called Loshiya. The middle one, Lopchuo. The youngest, Akchin-Hondo. They had nothing to do, and the eldest said:

"Let us sing songs, let us try out our voices. I will begin."

And he sang:

"Loshiy-a! Shiya! Loshiya!"

He finished and praised himself:

"I have a fine voice. Now, you try," he said to the middle one.

And the middle one sang:

"Lopchu-o! Chuo! Lopchuo!"

He finished and said:

"I sing well, too! Let us hear our youngest brother now."

And the youngest sang:

"Akchin-hondo! Hondo-hondo! Akchin!"

He finished. His brothers said:

"Well, his song is pretty good, too. Now let us sing all together."

They started. But each sang his own, and no song would come of it. The eldest got angry at the youngest, the youngest at the middle one, the middle one both at the eldest and the youngest.

"Why do you sing your own names? Sing mine! Then we shall have a fine song."

"Your name doesn't make a good song! Sing mine!" cried the eldest.

"And I don't even want to hear your names!" cried the youngest. "My own is best!"

And he began:

"Akchin-akchin-akchin-hondo! Hondo-hondo-do-do-akchin!"

The eldest and the middle brothers jumped on him and began to beat him. He struck back.

They turned over the kettle and the water put out the fire in the hearth. Rolling over the floor, they broke their arrows.

The eldest said:

"It isn't good to fight in the tent. Let's go out!"

The brothers went out and continued their fight on the grass. The eldest threw the youngest to the ground. The youngest lay on his back, his face up, and suddenly he saw the starry sky. He shouted:

"Wait, brothers! There's trouble coming!"

"What trouble? Where?" cried the eldest and the middle brothers.

The youngest jumped up and pointed at the stars in the sky.

"Look! Strangers are coming! They're carrying burning willow twigs to light their way. They mean to wage war on us!"

The brothers got frightened:

"We must run away! There are only three of us, and they are so many!"

They ran down to the river, jumped into their boat, and seized the oars. But they rowed just as they had sung. One pulled forward, the other back, and the third let the oars drag in the water, neither forward, nor back.

The boat turned around and around in the same spot. Waters plashed against its sides. And the brothers thought that their boat was flying like a bird down the river.

The eldest looked up and said:

"They're chasing us!"

Again they rowed. After a time, the deep blue sky began to turn gray. The stars began to fade. The middle one looked up and cried:

"They seem to be falling behind!"

They waved the oars some more. The air grew brighter. The stars disappeared. The youngest threw his head back and looked up. He could no longer see the burning willow branches in the hands of the enemy warriors.

"They've fallen far behind now."

"I know why they fell behind," said the eldest. "They must be plundering our tent."

"Yes, that's what they are doing," said the middle one.

"They will carry off our kettle and our furs! What shall we do?" wailed the youngest.

Suddenly they caught sight of a tent on the river bank. It was a large, handsome tent.

"This must be the tent of the enemy warriors," said the eldest.

"No one else's!" said the middle one. "Of course it's theirs."

"Well, if they are looting our tent, we'll loot theirs!" cried the youngest and jumped out of the boat.

The two others jumped out after him, and they ran, shouting, toward the enemy's tent.

They broke the poles of which the tent was made, tore off the skins that covered them. They seized the kettle and carried it off to their boat, and returned to where the tent had stood. They began to turn over its contents. The youngest found a bow. He raised it and shouted:

"But this is my bow! I made it myself!"

"Impossible! You're saying foolish things," the eldest cried angrily.

But just then he saw his own bow.

"Look," he poked the middle one, "Perhaps Akchin-Hondo is not so foolish, after all. I have found my bow, too."

And the middle brother, whose name was Lopchuo, had a third bow in his hands. He looked at it, and shook his head.

"Well, it appears that the bows are ours. Could the tent be ours too?"

They took up the skins they had piled on the side, and began to recognize them too.

"This is the skin of the deer I killed!"

"And this is the deer I killed!"

"And this is the bearskin our father left us!"

The brothers looked at one another in amazement. Then they asked:

"But how could this be? We rowed all night, and in the end we came to our own tent!"

They thought and thought, and they decided that

there was only one explanation: some shaman must have been so envious of their song that he bewitched them and sent a fog to cloud their eyes and their minds. In the future, they said, they would make sure no shaman would ever hear them sing.

THE MAIDEN
AND THE MOON

A Chukchi Tale

here was among the Chukchi people a man who had a daughter. The girl was a good helper to her father. Every summer she took their herd of deer to grazing fields far from the camp. Every winter she took the herd still farther, where the deer could find enough lichen and moss. Once in a long while she went back to the camp in her reindeer sled to replenish her food supplies.

One night her reindeer raised his head, looked up into the sky, and said:

"Look, look!"

The girl looked up and saw the Moon coming down from the sky in a sled drawn by heavenly reindeer.

"Where is he going? What does he want?" asked the girl.

"He wants to catch you and take you back with him!" said her deer.

The girl was frightened.

"What shall I do? He will carry me off to the sky!"

Her deer pawed the snow with his hoof until there was a little hollow. And he said:

"Sit down here, hurry!"

The girl crouched down in the hollow, and the deer covered her with snow. No girl, only a snowdrift!

The Moon came down, stopped his reindeer, climbed out of his sled, and walked this way and that, looking for the girl. But she was nowhere to be seen. He walked up to the mound of snow, but he never guessed what it was.

"How can this be?" the Moon wondered. "Where did the girl disappear? I cannot find her! I'll go back now and come down again. Next time I'll surely find her and carry her off!"

He sat down in his sled and his reindeer sped him back into the sky.

As soon as the Moon had left, the girl's deer scraped away the snow.

The girl came out and said:

"Let's hurry to the camp! Or else the Moon will see me and come down once more. And I may not be able to hide so easily again."

She sat down in her sled, and her deer sped across

the tundra. They raced into the camp, and the girl ran into her tent. But her father was not home. Who would help her?

And the deer urged her to hurry:

"You must hide, quickly, or the Moon will come racing after us!"

"But where can I hide?"

"I'll turn you into something else! What about a stone?"

"He will know!"

"I will turn you into a hammer!"

"He will know!"

"I'll turn you into one of the poles in the tent!"

"He will know!"

"A hair in the skin that covers the tent!"

"He will know, he will know!"

"But what else? A lamp?"

"Good! Good!"

"Sit down, then!"

The girl sat down. The deer stamped his hoof on the ground, and she turned into a lamp. The lamp burned brightly, filling the tent with light.

But just as the girl was turning into a lamp, the Moon looked down from the sky and searched for her among her herd. She was not there, and he came speeding to the camp.

He tied his reindeer to the post, entered the tent,

and began to look for the girl. He searched and he searched, and could not find her. He looked between the poles, examined all the household utensils, every hair in the skins, every twig under the bedding, every inch of ground in the tent. The girl was not anywhere!

And the lamp was the only thing he did not notice, because the lamp was bright, and the Moon was bright.

"Strange," said the Moon. "Where can she be? I guess I must go back without finding her."

He went out of the tent and untied his reindeer. Then he sat down on his sled. But just as he was going to leave, the girl ran over to the entrance of her tent, put out her head between the skins, laughed, and shouted to the Moon:

"Here I am! Here I am!"

The Moon jumped off his sled and ran back into the tent. But the girl had turned herself once more into a lamp.

The Moon started searching again. He searched among the twigs and leaves, among the bits of earth on the ground, the ashes in the hearth. The girl was not anywhere!

"How can this be? Where is she? Where could she disappear? I suppose I shall have to go back empty-handed!"

He stepped out of the tent and began to untie his

reindeer. And once again the girl leaned out of the tent, laughing and shouting:

"Here I am! Here I am!"

The Moon rushed back and started searching again.

He searched and searched, he turned everything upside down, and still he could not find her.

He tired himself out with all that work. He grew thin and weak. He could barely move his feet now, or raise his hands.

And now the girl was no longer afraid of him. She assumed her former shape, jumped out of the tent threw the Moon on his back, and tied his hands and feet.

"Oh!" moaned the Moon. "You'll kill me now! All right, then, kill me. It is my own fault, I wanted to carry you off from the earth. But before I die, take me into the tent, let me warm myself a little, I am badly chilled . . ."

"How can you be chilled?" the girl wondered. "You are always out in the open, you have no tent, you have no home. No, stay out now, too! You don't need to go into the tent!"

The Moon began to plead with the girl:

"If I must be forever homeless, then let me go! I will amuse your people. Let me go! I will light your people's way. Let me go! I will turn night into day. Let me go! I will measure the year for your people.

First I will be the Moon of the old bull, then the Moon of the birth of calves, then the Moon of the waters, then the Moon of the leaves, then the Moon of warmth, then the Moon of the peeling of horns, then the Moon of the mating of wild deer, then the Moon of the early winter, then the Moon of the shortening days."

"And if I let you go and you get strong again, and your arms and legs get strong, will you chase me still, will you try again to carry me off into the sky?"

"No, no, I won't! I'll never come down from my heavenly path again! Let me go—I will light up the sky and the earth!"

She let him go—and he lit up the night.

THE NINWITS

A Koryak Tale

hree women went into the tundra to pick berries. There were many blueberries and cloudberries that year. The women picked and picked, going farther and farther from their camp. They stopped only when the sun began to set and it began to turn dark.

A hunter could find his way even at night. But women worked mostly in the camp and did not know how to tell one place from another. They lost their way, but went on and on—perhaps toward the camp, perhaps away from it.

One fell behind, another went off to the side, and all three became frightened. They began to call to one another, and came together again. After that, they did not separate.

One of them said:

"Let us shout. Someone may hear us and answer us from the camp."

And she shouted:

"Eh-hey! Eh-hey!"

"E-e-hey!" came from somewhere far away.

Was it an echo, or had someone heard them?

Now all three shouted:

"We're here! Come this way! He-ere!"

"Coming," someone answered.

Soon they heard footsteps and laughed with relief. Help was near. Suddenly three men appeared before them as if out of nowhere. The women did not know them, they were from some other camp. The women huddled together: those men looked very strange! Their heads were large, their legs short, and their arms long.

The youngest of the women whispered:

"Let's run away!"

But the middle one said:

"They'll catch us!"

The eldest took them by the hand:

"Sillies! Why should we refuse their help?"

And the men said:

"Ho-ho! You called us yourselves! Now come with us to our camp."

Their camp was nearby—a single large yurt in the

bare tundra. In the yurt there was a blind old woman, evidently the mother of the men.

"You brought them?" she asked in a hoarse voice.

"We did!" answered one. "The quarry came into our hands of its own will!"

"A rich quarry, too!" boasted the second man.

"We'll have a good meal!" laughed the third one.

The women understood that they had fallen into the hands of Ninwits, who ate humans.

Meantime, the old woman began to make a fire in the yurt and hung a large kettle of water over it. The men took out their knives and began to sharpen them.

The women did not look at one another, but each had the same thought:

If they would let us live at least till morning.

At that moment the eldest Ninwit yawned and said:

"O-haw! I'm sleepy! It will take till morning to kill them and cook them. Let's leave it for tomorrow."

"Let's," said the middle one. "When you know you have food waiting, it's the same as if you have eaten. You have good dreams."

The younger Ninwit made a face, but he did not say anything.

The Ninwits tied the women to the poles that held up the yurt, and went to sleep. The blind old woman also crawled under the animal hides on the floor and went to sleep.

The fire in the hearth went out. Only the coals still glowed here and there. It was quiet and dark in the yurt. But the women did not sleep. The eldest one began to stretch and twist her hands, till the leather strips that bound her loosened a little. She freed one hand, and pulled the other out easily. Then she bent down and untied the strips that bound her feet. After that she ran to her friend and untied her, and together they quickly freed the third one.

"Hurry, let's run away!" whispered the youngest woman.

"Wait," said the eldest. "First, tie the Ninwits' fur robes to the poles. If they wake up at night they'll think we are still here."

They did as she told them and ran out of the yurt. The eldest said, "I'll follow in a second!" She was a clever woman. She thought to herself: "The mother of the Ninwits is surely not an ordinary woman! And everything she has here is not ordinary. I will take a few things with me—they may prove useful on the way."

She picked up a stone scraper, a coal from the fire, and the little piece of ice which lay in a cup near the old woman's head and never melted. Then she stole to the door.

Her friends were waiting for her impatiently, and the three of them ran from the yurt. They ran as fast as they could, driven by fear.

After a while, the youngest Ninwit woke up and thought:

"Why wait till morning? I am hungry now."

He got up, took a knife, and went to one of the poles. With his hands he felt for the woman's head, but what a strange thing! The robe was there, but the head was not. He went to the second pole, and found the same thing. He tried the third, and again the robe was there, but no one was inside it.

The Ninwit began to shout:

"Get up, brothers! Our quarry is gone!"

They jumped up and set out to catch the women.

They followed the scent like dogs, their noses smelling out the way. They had short legs, but they ran fast, leaping over hillocks, trampling the bushes on the way.

The women ran too. But they did not know they were chased until they heard the Ninwits' footsteps close behind them.

"Oh, they will catch us," said the youngest.

"We are lost!" cried the second.

But the eldest snatched the stone scraper from her pocket and flung it behind her. A high, steep mountain rose where it fell, between the women and the pursuing Ninwits. When the pursuers came to the mountain, they roared with anger and began to climb it. Before they were halfway up the eldest said:

"I am out of breath. Those women were too thin, anyway! Nothing but skin and bones! I will not waste my strength chasing after them."

And he went back.

His two brothers continued to climb. They reached the top and rolled down the other side. Again they ran after the women. And again they were just about to overtake them.

"Do you have anything else?" the youngest woman asked the eldest.

"I do indeed. I was not improvident, like you."

And she threw the glowing coal behind her.

Suddenly everything behind them caught fire. Tongues of flame swayed and ran from tree to tree, from bush to bush, like waves in the sea. And the fire lit everything around so brightly that the women could see their home camp in the distance. With renewed strength they hurried toward it.

The women ran before the fire, the Ninwits behind it. When they reached the fire, they stopped.

"Neither a deer nor a wolf will walk into fire. Neither a squirrel nor a dog will go near it. Should I, then, be more stupid than they?" said the middle Ninwit and turned back.

But the youngest Ninwit shut his eyes and rushed into the fire. Every time he stepped on a hot coal, he

jumped. When his robe caught fire, he threw it off. When his hair caught fire, he beat it with his hands to put out the fire.

At last he came through, black as a charred log, but still alive. And now, even more furious than before, he ran after the women, until they heard the thunder of his feet just behind them. The camp was very near now, but they would not be able to reach it before the Ninwit caught them.

And the eldest woman threw the last remaining thing behind her. The piece of ice fell on the ground, and a wide river flowed where it fell. While the Ninwit stood on the other bank, thinking how he might cross the river, the women reached their home camp.

By that time it was daylight, and the women saw their menfolk coming out of the camp.

"Where are you going?" they asked the men.

And the men answered:

"You don't know anything! There is suddenly a new river flowing past the camp; we are going to fish."

"Don't go! There is a Ninwit across the river," the women cried after them.

"What do we care about Ninwits!" said the men. "It will be good to have some fish for supper."

The women walked toward the yurts, but suddenly they stopped.

"We left our baskets full of berries in the tundra!" said the youngest.

"We'll get up early tomorrow morning and go out to look for them," said the eldest.

The third one nodded:

"It would be a pity to lose the baskets! And all those berries, too!"

And each went to her own yurt.

In the meantime the men were already fishing in the river. The Ninwit saw them from the other bank and shouted:

"Hey, people! Did you see three women who got across the river?"

"We did," the men answered.

"How did they get across?"

"Very simply! They drank up all the water in one place and walked across the dry spot."

"They are right," the Ninwit said to himself. "It's simple enough."

He lay down on the bank and began to drink the water. He drank and drank, until his belly swelled up, until he could not drink any more and could not move from the spot.

And down the river floated leaves, twigs, bits of grass. The Ninwit began to yell at them:

"Don't come near me! Don't touch me! I will burst!"

But the leaves and the twigs did not listen to him,

they came and came his way. The Ninwit began to blow at them to drive them away. He bent over the water, and his heavy belly pulled him down.

And the river carried him along, together with the leaves and twigs. He floated down and down until he reached his camp. He just barely managed to get out onto the bank. There he lay down and puffed.

His brother Ninwits jumped out of the yurt and saw his belly rising above the ground like a hill. And they asked with envy:

"So you caught all three of them! And you ate them all up?"

"Naturally, I did," boasted the youngest Ninwit. "I had a fine feast—look how full my belly is!"

"Why didn't you bring us something, too? Why didn't you think of us?"

"Why should I think of you?" the youngest cried angrily. "I caught them, so they were mine to eat!"

THE LOST SONG

An Eskimo Tale

I n Spring two snow buntings came to the cliffs near Bering Strait and built themselves a nest on a high crag over the sea.

The she-bunting laid an egg and sat down to hatch it. She never flew off the nest, afraid the cold winds might chill the egg. She covered the egg with her body against the driving rain. She did not eat enough, and did not sleep enough.

At last a little son hatched out of the egg, a fine, pretty little son. Nobody on the whole coast had a nicer chick. There was only one thing wrong with him —he was too noisy.

His parents now really had no time to eat or drink or sleep. When the father flew away to look for food, the mother sang her son to sleep. When the mother flew away for a short while, the father stayed in the nest and took care of the son.

One day the little mother bunting sat on the edge of the nest and sang to her son:

"Cheer up, cheer up! Whose little claws are these?
 Cheer up, cheer up! Whose little wings are these?
 Cheer up, cheer up! Whose little head is this?
 Whose little darling eyes?
 Cheer up, cheer up, cheer up!"

A raven flew by, heard the song, sat down nearby and began to listen. The more he listened, the more he liked it. He liked it so much, he would not go away. And he begged the mother bunting:

"Give me that song! Give me that song!"

"Oh, no!" said the mother bunting. "I cannot give it to you. It is the only song we have, we have no other."

"Please, please," begged the raven. "I cannot live without that song now."

"And my son cannot fall asleep without it. Don't even ask me, I won't give it to you!"

The raven got angry.

"If you don't give it to me when I ask, I'll take it from you by force!"

He rushed at the bunting, tore the song from her mouth, and flew away.

The baby bunting started crying and screaming. And the mother bunting started crying.

The father bunting came back from the hunt and found his son screaming, and his wife in tears.

"What happened?" he asked. "What terrible misfortune struck?"

"A terrible, terrible misfortune," answered the mother bunting. "A raven came flying and carried off our song. Now our son won't fall asleep, he'll cry himself weak! How are we going to live?"

The father bunting flew into a rage. His eyes flashed, and he stamped his foot.

"Give me my hunting mittens, my bow, and my arrows! I will find the raven, I will pluck the song from his throat!"

He flew and flew, and saw many birds, but he did not see the raven. He caught sight of a grouse running among the stones, he heard a plover whistling, but no ravens. At last he found a whole flock of ravens on a cliff. He alighted nearby, put his arrow in his bow, pulled the string, and waited. If any raven sang his song, he would be struck down by the bunting's arrow.

But the ravens were busy with their own affairs.

The old were sunning themselves or chatting. The young played games. The young fellows whispered into their sweethearts' ears. And nobody sang—either the bunting song or any other. At times one or another would caw, but what kind of a song is that?

The father bunting flew on. He flew and he circled around, until he saw a raven sitting on a tree, all alone in the branches, with his beak up, his eyes shut, rocking from side to side, and singing for all he was worth:

"Cheer up, cheer up! Whose little claws are these?
Cheer up! Whose little wings are these?
Whose little head is this?
Whose little darling eyes?"

He'd finish, and immediately start again:

"Cheer up, cheer up! Whose little claws are these?
Whose little wings?"

"There he is, the robber!" the father bunting cried. "The stealer of the best song in the world!"

He sat down on a branch of that same tree, drew his bow, and let the arrow fly. The arrow slipped over the raven's stiff, shiny feathers and fell onto the ground. The raven did not even notice it and did not open his eyes. He was aware of nothing in the world except his beautiful song.

Then the father bunting seized all the arrows in his

quiver, held them between his fingers, and began to send them at the thief by threes or fours.

And the raven still sang:
"Cheer up, cheer up! Whose little claws are these?
 Oh, whose little wings?
 Oh, oh, something hit me in the side!
 Oh, whose little head is this?
 Oh, oh, something's pricking my chest!
 Oh, whose little darling eyes?
 Ouch! Oh! Ouch! I can't any more! Caw! Caw!"

And the song dropped out of his beak.

The father bunting quickly snatched it and flew back to his nest.

As he came near, he heard his son screaming, his wife crying.

"Don't scream, don't cry," The father bunting said to them. "I got our song back from the evil raven. Here it is!"

And the mother bunting caught it, overjoyed, and began to sing. The baby bunting quieted down and fell asleep.

Ever since then, whenever buntings see a raven flying by, they stop singing, afraid even to open their beaks. And that is how their song has been preserved. And all the buntings sing it to their noisy children to this day.

THE HUNTER
AND THE TIGER

A Nivkh Tale

ne day a hunter took his little son with him to the taiga to hunt sable.

They came to the taiga, chopped down some young fir trees, and built a hunter's hut near an old birch with a thick trunk and forked branches.

The father said:

"It is dangerous and frightening here, in the taiga . . . ."

"I am not afraid of anyone!" said the son. "I have no fear at all! Whoever attacks us, I will get the best of him!"

The father chided him:

"Don't speak like that. You are still small, there's not

much strength in you. You'd better say: I am afraid of everybody!"

"No," said the son. "I won't say that! If I lack strength, I'll make up for it by agility and skill. I can deal with all enemies!"

He had barely finished when a huge tiger came padding to the hut. He glanced inside and asked:

"Who is boasting here that he will get the best of anybody?"

The father saw the tiger and began to shake with terror. He stammered out:

"I didn't say that. . . . I am afraid of everybody. . . . And I'm terribly afraid of you. . . . Turn your head, don't look at me. Let me out of the hut!"

The tiger turned his head and let the hunter out.

The hunter ran away as fast as he could go.

The tiger looked into the hut again and asked:

"Who was it, then, who boasted that he could overcome all enemies? Who is it here who's not afraid of anyone?"

The boy was not frightened, and answered:

"I am not afraid of anyone! I can overcome anyone who attacks me!"

The tiger said:

"In that case, let us wrestle. If you are stronger, you will kill me. If I am stronger, I will eat you up!"

And the tiger put his head and paws into the hut, preparing to seize the boy.

The boy jumped up, intending to leap over the tiger. But the tiger raised his head and would not let him out:

"Well, what will you do now?"

The boy tried to slip out under him. But the tiger crouched down and lowered his head.

Again the boy could not get out.

Then he decided to trick the tiger. He pretended that he wanted to slip out under the tiger again. The tiger crouched, lowered his head, and waited.

The boy made a sudden leap, and jumped across him before the tiger knew what was happening. Then the boy quickly climbed to the very top of the birch tree.

The tiger leaped after him, but the boy was too fast, and the tiger got his head caught in the fork of the tree and hung there, helpless. He clawed at the birch-bark, beat his tail, and growled, but he could not free himself.

The boy climbed down from the tree.

"I said I wasn't afraid of anyone, I said I'd get the better of any enemy!"

The tiger was silent. He could not say anything. He even stopped beating his tail. He was dying.

The boy looked and looked at the tiger, and thought to himself:

"Why should the poor tiger die?"

He took an axe, climbed up the birch tree again, and chopped off the branch that held the tiger's head.

The tiger dropped to the ground, and lay there motionless for a long time. At last he recovered and rose to his feet. He stood under the birch tree, looking up at the boy who sat astride a branch, and he did not go away. The boy asked him:

"Why don't you go away? Go!"

The tiger looked at him and said:

"You are brave, and you are agile. And you are good, too. You did not let me die. Come down, I will take you home. You'll be my guest, and I will give you a good present."

The boy climbed down. The tiger told him to get up on his back, and he started out.

They crossed the taiga, climbed up and down mountains, going on and on until they reached the highest mountain of all. The tiger climbed this mountain, to the very top. And there the boy saw that the place was inhabited. There was a large winter yurt, and many dogs on leashes. All around the yurt hung tiger skins on poles stuck in the ground.

The boy climbed down from the tiger's back and looked at him, but there was no longer any tiger. Before him stood a tall young man, and a tiger skin lay on the ground next to him.

The boy was so astonished that he did not know what to think.

And the young man hung the tiger skin on a pole and said:

"We take the shape of tigers only down below. Here we become men. Come with me into the yurt."

They entered and saw a gray-haired old man sitting there. He glanced at the boy and asked the young man:

"Whom did you bring to me?"

"Father, this hunter saved my life. I thought that I was stronger than he, and challenged him to a fight. But he is clever and agile. He jumped over me and climbed a tree. And, when I tried to catch him, I was caught, myself, in a fork of the tree. If he had not chopped the branch down. I would have died and never returned home to you. You would have no son now!"

The old man nodded and said:

"We'll give him a good present for that!"

He went out and brought a large sled. Then he began to pile sable skins on the sled. He piled them and piled them. There were so many, you could not count them! Then he said:

"Now you can go home."

"But how can I go?" asked the boy. "I don't know the way, I'll get lost in the taiga."

"You won't get lost. The sled will take you there."

And it was true. The sled moved by itself. They came down from the high mountain, then up and down other mountains, then across the taiga. It was a long journey, but at last they came to the father's yurt. And the father was sitting in the yurt, grieving. He carved a little figure of his son from a piece of wood, and looked at it, and cried, thinking to himself:

"The tiger ate him up! I am alone now. . . . How will I live without my son?"

And the son was standing near the yurt, calling his father. The father came out, looked up, and did not believe his eyes. Before him stood his son, alive and well, and with a sled piled with more sable skins than all the hunters of their camp could get in five years!

THE GOOD SON

A Nanay Tale

It was a long, long time ago. Many years have gone by since it happened. Where rivers once flowed there are now high mountains. Where high mountains stood, there are now wide rivers.

In a certain camp there lived a woman, Vaida, who had a little son. The son's name was Anga. Anga had no father. His father had been killed by a tiger.

One day Vaida fell sick. She got worse and worse, until she just lay in her yurt and could not get up.

Neighboring women came to visit her and said:

"The evil spirit, Buseu, sent her this sickness and is tormenting her! Buseu must be driven out!"

They called the villagers to the sick woman's yurt, put out the light, and tried to frighten and drive out the evil spirit. They banged on iron kettles, shook their rattles, and shouted loudly: "Ga-a-a! Gaa-aa-gaa!" But nothing helped.

They called the medicine man, the shaman. The shaman came in his horned hat, warmed his tambourine over the fire to make it tighter and more resonant, and began to beat it with a stick with all his might. He beat it and he danced all around the yurt. He jumped from side to side. He chanted magical incantations. The iron bells and clappers on his belt rang and clanked.

For a long time the shaman beat his tambourine, for a long time he circled around the sick woman, but he could not help her either.

Then an old woman said:

"She would get well if somebody got for her a scale from the body of the serpent Ogloma and a hair from the fur of the big bear, the Master of all the bears. But this is difficult and dangerous! To find the serpent Ogloma you must cross the entire taiga. And when you find him, there is a new danger, for there is another serpent, Simun, who lives next to Ogloma. Simun attacks everybody, even Ogloma. If anyone dares to come near him, he breathes fire and turns his hands to coal!"

Anga listened and remembered everything, but said nothing.

Another old woman spoke about the bear:

"Nobody is brave enough to visit the Master of the Bears. He lives on a high mountain, in a deep cave. It is difficult to climb that mountain, and it is fearful to come near the Master of the Bears. Where can you find a hero who will dare it?"

The old women shook their heads, talked some more, and went home. The mother and her son remained alone in the yurt. The mother lay moaning, looking at her son, and crying bitterly.

"I am sick, I shall never get up again. How will you live alone?"

But the boy said to her:

"Don't cry! I will cure you. I will get a scale of the serpent Ogloma and a hair of the Master of the Bears!"

"You are too small to go on such a journey! You'll perish!"

"I have no fear," answered Anga. "I will go! Perhaps I will not perish!"

He sharpened his spear, took a large kettle and a long leather rope, and started out. On the way, he pulled off bits of resin from the trunks of firs and pines, and put them in the kettle.

He walked a very long time, till he came to a river. He stopped and looked around. Near the river grew a huge tree, thicker and higher than all the others. Its foliage shut out the sun during the day and the moon at night. And everything around the tree was scorched.

This was where the serpent Simun lived.

Anga began to gather moss. He gathered a great pile of moss and wrapped himself in it, tying it around with his long leather rope. After that he stepped into the river and dipped down, head and all, until the moss was wet through and through. He came out on the river bank, with water dripping on the ground from all that moss. Then he boldly went up to the tree and began to bang his spear against the kettle. He raised a great noise. All the birds flew out and scattered far away. All the animals ran far away and hid themselves.

The serpent Simun heard the noise and crawled out of his nest in the tree. He slithered toward Anga, hissing furiously, leaving a red trail behind him, where the grass and even the stones were burning.

The serpent Simun crept up to Anga, opened his maw, and breathed a blast of flame at him. But Anga was unharmed, protected by the wet moss.

Simun breathed another blast. Steam rose from Anga and spread like a fog all around. Anga heaved up the kettle with the pine resin and threw it straight into the serpent's maw. The resin melted and filled Simun's throat, and choked him to death.

In a little while another serpent came to Anga and said:

"I am the serpent Ogloma. I have fought Simun all my life and could not vanquish him. He devoured all my children. You have helped me, you rid me of the evil Simun. Tell me what I can give you as reward!"

"I don't need anything," said Anga. "I want only a single scale from your body to cure my mother!"

Ogloma gave Anga a scale, and he went on.

He walked for a long time. No one can tell how long he walked. At last he came to a high mountain. He wanted to look up at its top, and his hat fell off his head, so high was that mountain.

Anga began to climb it. He climbed from ledge to ledge, caught hold of every rock and every projection, scratched his hands to blood, but he never thought about himself. He remembered one thing: his sick mother lying in their yurt.

Who knows how long he climbed, but finally he reached a deep cave. He entered the cave and saw an enormous bear, the Master of all the bears, sleeping there, his paws outspread, moaning.

Anga looked at him, and saw a twig stuck like a splinter deep in the bear's hind paw.

He felt sorry for the bear. He tied his rope to the end of the twig, tugged at it with all his strength, and pulled it out of the bear's paw.

The Master of the Bears woke up, saw Anga, and said:

"For three years I have suffered and could not remove the splinter! And now my suffering is over! You rid me of it. What can I give you in exchange?"

Anga said to him:

"Give me only one hair from your body, to cure my mother. I need nothing else!"

The Master of the Bears gave him a hair, and Anga hurried back to his encampment. Like a young deer he raced across the taiga!

He ran into the yurt and gave his mother the scale of the serpent Ogloma and the hair of the Master of the Bears. She laid them against her body and got well at once.

From then on Anga was considered the bravest and best man in the whole camp.

Who knows where it happened, near or far—but this is the end of the tale!